THE WOOLLEN MILL BUILDINGS IN THE HILLFOOTS AREA

BRIAN A PARK

Forth Naturalist and Historian

Published by Forth Naturalist & Historian Editorial Board,
The University of Stirling, 1984   Reprint, 1996

A study for the Alexander Main Scholarship
by Brian A. Park, 1979

British Library, Cataloguing in Publication Data
Park, Brian A.
Woollen mill buildings in the Hillfoots area
 1. Historic buildings – Scotland – Clackmannan (Central Region)
 2. Clackmannan (Central Region, Scotland) – Buildings
 1. Title
941-3' 15   DA880-C5
ISBN 0-9506962-1-8

c Brian A. Park

Cover design by G. Thomson –
Illustration – The Clock Mill, Tillicoultry

Printed by Meigle Printers Ltd., Galashiels

Wooollen Mills of the Hillfoots

The development of the textile industry in the Hillfoots, spanning as it does more than two centuries, provides us simultaneously with a graphic illustration of the ephemeral nature of man's activities and the reminder of the value of those parts of our heritage which have survived. Dwarfed by the scenic splendour of a natural landscape a million times more ancient, the heart of the once thriving industry has been eaten away by the "acid rain" of economic recession and its fabric eroded by wind, weather and redevelopment.

This publication, coming as it does during a period of intense re-building in the locality, serves a number of important functions. A scholarly work, it provides an accurate and detailed picture of the development of the industry and the extent and location of its remains. Highly readable and richly illustrated, it is a stimulating source of general interest and reference. Lastly, with precision and modesty, it outlines the limits of the research which had been undertaken and highlights areas for future investigation.

Its author, Brian Park, must be congratulated for bringing these functions together so successfully. I am sure that he will be rewarded, not only by the widespread appreciation of this publication, but also by the appearance, in time, of further work stimulated by it.

Contents

INTRODUCTION

ACKNOWLEDGEMENTS

SECTION 1   Hillfoots Woollen Industry

                     Introduction, Background up to the 19th century   page 1

                     19th century onwards   page 6

SECTION 2   Mill Buildings of the Past

                     Menstrie - Archibald's Mill; Elmbank Mill;
                           Forthvale Mill.   page 15

                     Alva - Burn Mill; Braehead Mill; Harrower's Mill;
                         Horse Mill; Strude Mills; Cobblecrook Mill;
                         Meadow Mill; Brook Street Mill; Brookfield
                         Mills; Other mills.   page 20

                     Tillicoultry - Waulk Mill; Castle Mills;
                                 Middletoun Mill; Craigfoot Mill;
                                 Company Mill; Dawson's Mill;
                                 New Castle Mill; Henderson's Mill;
                                 Marshall's Mill; Spinning Mill;
                                 Mills at Devonside.   page 28

                     Dollar - Woollen Mill at Dollar   page 37

SECTION 3   Water Power System at Tillicoultry   page 39

SECTION 4   Existing Mill Buildings

                     Menstrie   page 49

                     Alva   page 61

                     Tillicoultry   page 120

                     (for lists see following page)

APPENDIX   Drawing of water power system at Tillicoultry

Introduction

The Alexander Mair Scholarship was originally awarded for a study of the historic industrial buildings of Central Region, however, the number of buildings and building types which this covered would have meant only a very limited reference to each. Since this descriptive cataloguing had already been done by John Hume*, it was felt that it would be of more value to concentrate on one specific area and building type.

Having already begun to visit the woollen mill buildings of Clackmannanshire, I spoke to John Hume who indicated that it was the intention of the Scottish Industrial Archaeology Survey to study the buildings in more depth and to produce measured drawings of them. Thereafter approval was given by the award committee to concentrate on these specific buildings with the intention of providing the information collected to the SIAS.

The study is primarily intended to provide a straightforward, factual description and photographic record of the woollen mill buildings which still exist in the area of Clackmannanshire immediately to the south of the Ochil Hills generally known as the Hillfoots (see map). While the buildings themselves are important, it is also necessary to place them in their historical context. In view of the fragmentary nature of the available information, a large part of the study concentrates on bringing together such material to provide a reasonably comprehensive background to the industrial development which necessitated the erection of such mill buildings.

The following is a brief synopsis of the study :

Section 1 considers the Hillfoots region in a national and international context with regard to developments in the textile trade leading up to the erection of specific mill buildings.

Section 2 gives a reasonably detailed account of the background to many of the mills which played a prominent role in the trade of the 19th century but which no longer exist.

Section 3 deals with the fascinating water power system at Tillicoultry which once operated many of the mills there. The discussion of the system is obviously limited in this study but the topic would provide an excellent basis for an in-depth industrial archaeology study.

Section 4 gives a verbal and photographic description of the mill buildings which remain and also a brief outline of their present use and condition.

---

* "The Industrial Archaeology of Scotland" (Vol.1) J.R.Hume Batsford. 1976

The limitation of time has meant that not every possible source of material has been covered. Notable among these are the local papers, The Alloa Circular and Hillfoots Record and the Alloa Advertiser, not all of which have been adequately catalogued. A tedious search through such would undoubtedly reveal much information, particularly on some of the dates about which there is some doubt. Several individuals who were recommended as being valuable founts of information have also proved impossible to contact within the available time. It should therefore be made clear that the study is by no means definitive - much scope remains for further researches in this area.

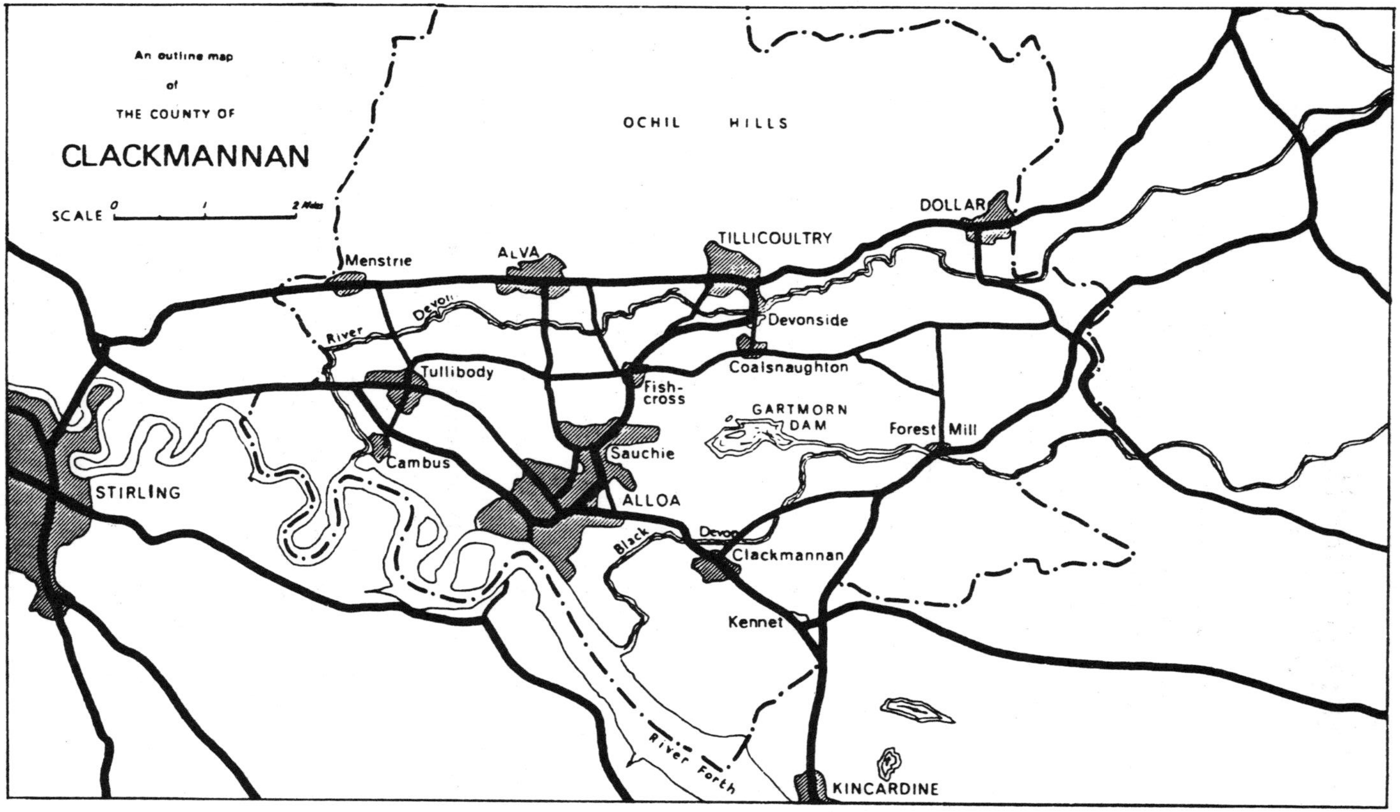

Menstrie, Alva, Tillicoultry and Dollar in relation to surrounding area.

Acknowledgements

A large number of individuals and organisations have assisted during the preparation of this report. The reason for including the following fairly comprehensive list is so that any making further researches in this area may have a ready list of contacts. It is hoped that this will initially be of help to the Scottish Industrial Archaeology Survey.

Thanks are due to :

Mrs Brodie and her staff at Central Region Archives (Stirling) and the staff of Alloa Library for assistance and also, in both cases, for providing tea and coffee !

Staff of the National Library of Scotland Map Room (Edinburgh).

Staff of Stirling Public Library and of Stirling University Library.

Mr Bracewell (architect) who provided much material - old books, photographs, drawings, etc. - and with whose permission the drawing of the water system at Tillicoultry is reproduced.

Miss Lawlor of the S.D.D. Historic Buildings Branch who, in the initial stages of the project, provided free of charge, copies of the statutory lists of historic buildings for the whole of Central Region (amounting to some 400 pages !).

Mr John Hume and Mr Graham Douglas of the Scottish Industrial Archaeology Survey who initially provided the stimulus to concentrate on the woollen mill buildings in Clackmannanshire and who have subsequently provided early O.S. maps and other helpful references.

New Lanark Conservation and Civic Trust who have allowed time off work in order to visit the mill buildings and in particular Mr Jim Arnold (manager) who has given additional encouragement.

Dr Frances J Shaw of the Scottish Record Office (West Register House) through whom arrangements were made to consult the records of Messrs. Patons & Baldwins, Alloa.

Mr Robert McIntyre of Nuneaton who took the trouble to arrange for me to consult his dissertation while his wife was in Scotland.

Mr Gavin Sprott, research assistant in the Country Life Archive of the National Museum of Antiquities (Edinburgh).

Mr Dawson of Menstrie who worked for many years in the buildings which were formerly woollen mills and who was able to cast his mind far enough back to provide useful information.

Dr K.J.H. Mackay of Stirling University who was able to refer to a number of helpful sources.

Mr Murray Dickie, local historian, who provided useful references early on. (unfortunately time made a later consultation with Mr Dickie impossible.)

Mr Duncan Sinclair (of D.C. Sinclair and Son, Clock Mill) who spent much time reminiscing and answering queries, particularly on the water power system at Tillicoultry.

Mr Bowie, chief engineer at Middleton Mill who provided a copy of a drawing of the mills in the ownership of R. Archibald and Sons in 1922, and also a plan of Devonvale Mills.

Visits to the mill buildings were arranged through the following :

Mr Tom Sinclair of the Clock Mill, Tillicoultry.
Mr R. Burt of Raymond Hodgson & Co. (Strude Mill).
M. Hunter of Raymond Hodgson & Co. (Ochilvale Mills).
Mr Paton (sen) of J.& D. Paton & Co. Ltd. (Paton's Mill).
Mrs Burnett of J. Hewitt & Co. Ltd. (Devonpark Mills)
Mr Crampton of Alva Youth Club (formerly woollen mill).
Mr Dempster & Mr Alan Johnston of Glen Alva Ltd. (Henry Street woollen mill).
Mr J.M. Thomson of Dolf Textiles (Henry Street woollen mill).
Mr I.D. Philip of McBean & Bishop Ltd. (Glentana Mills).
Mr A. Jeffrey of Sterling Warehouses Ltd. (Devonvale mills).
Mr Dewar of Dewar Brothers (Packaging) Ltd. (Oak Mill).
Mr Adie & Mr Mailer of Central Regional Council (Mill at Menstrie).

Existing Mill Buildings

Menstrie   Part of Elmbank Mills

Alva   Strude Mill
              Braehead Mill
              Handloom weaving mill, Brook Street
              Greenfield Mill
              Glentana Mills
              Burnside Mill
              Burnbrae Works
              Ochilvale Mills

Tillicoultry Paton's Mill
              Clock Mill
              Middleton Mill
              Devonvale Mill
              Oak Mill

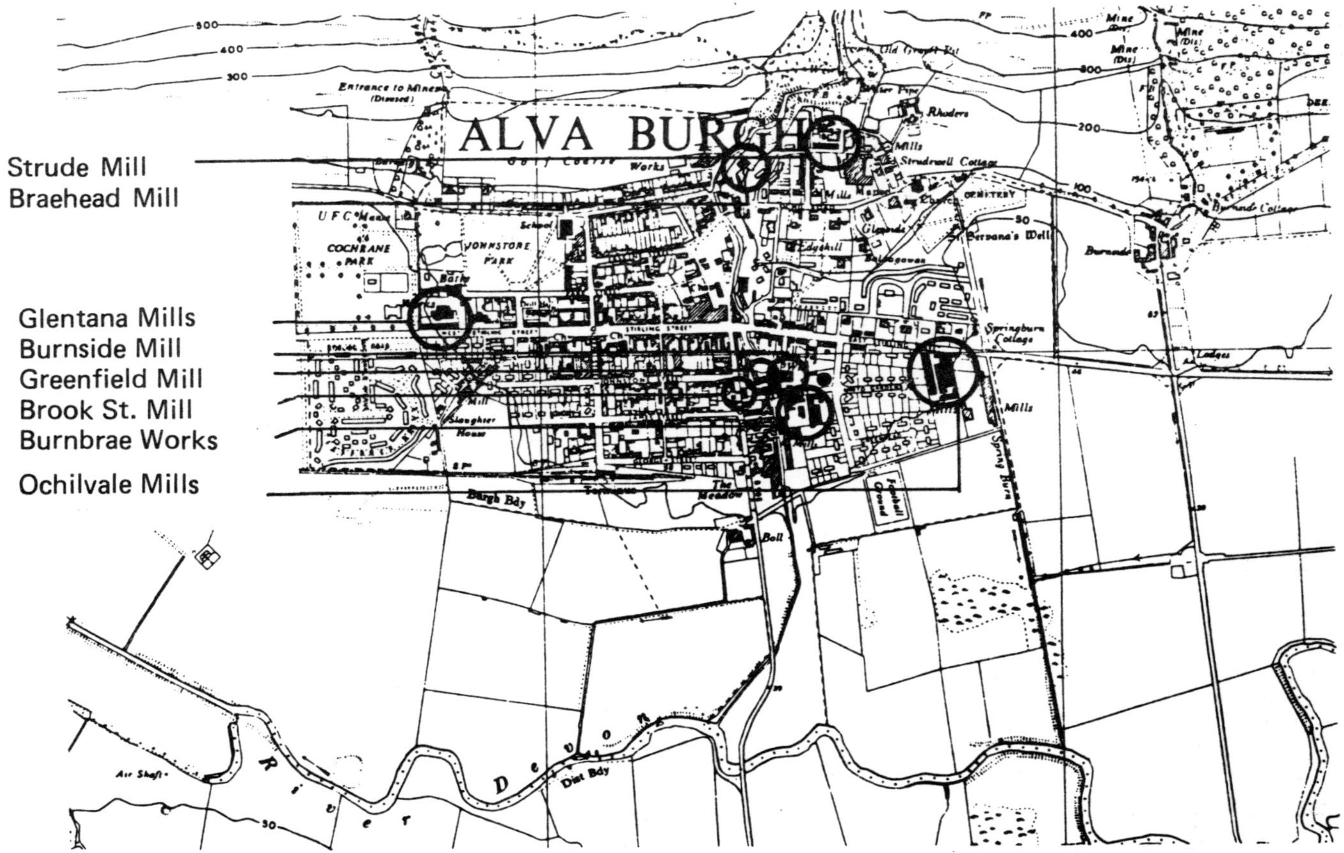

Strude Mill
Braehead Mill

Glentana Mills
Burnside Mill
Greenfield Mill
Brook St. Mill
Burnbrae Works
Ochilvale Mills

Location of existing mills in Alva.

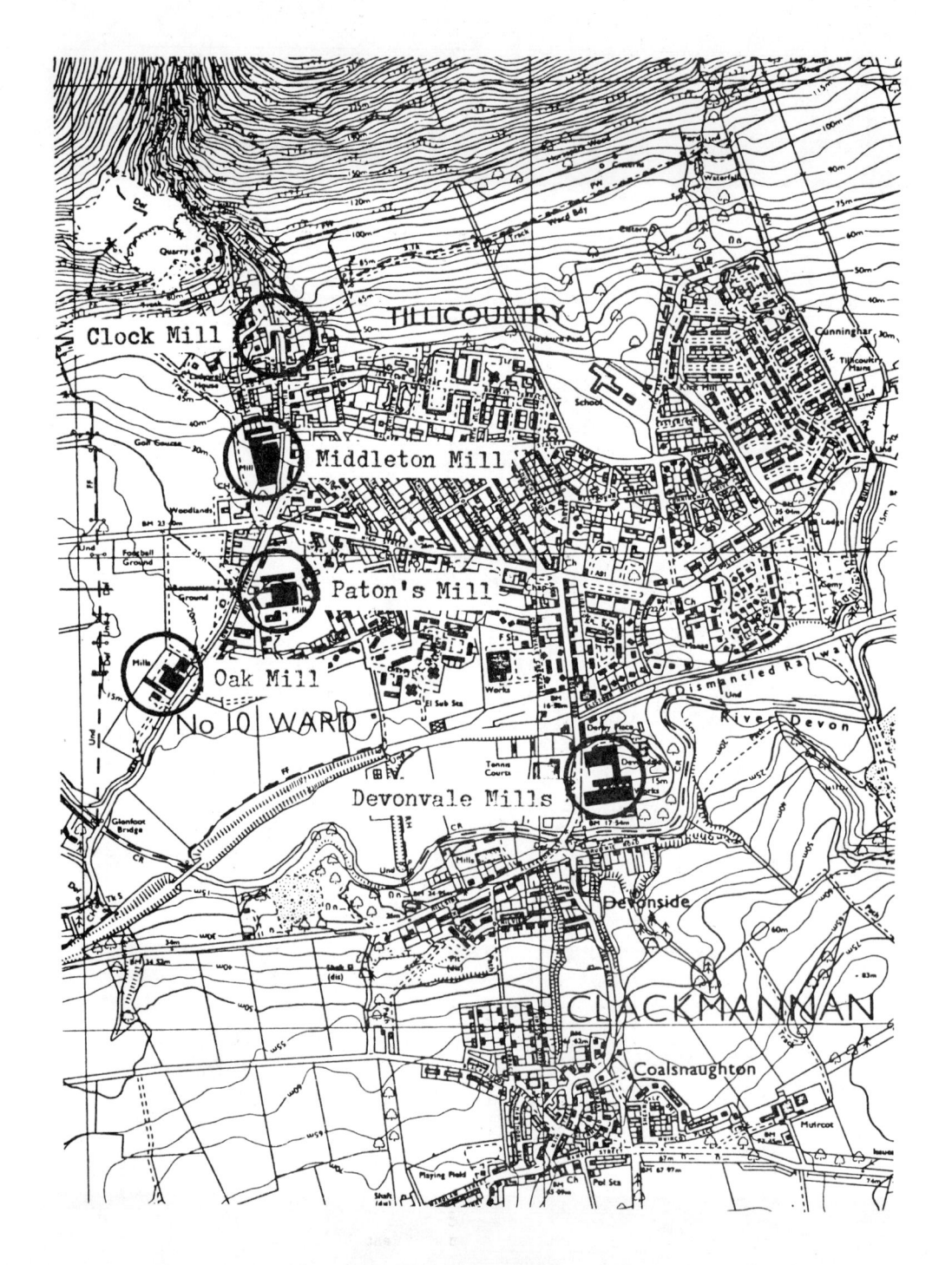

Location of remaining mills in Tillicoultry.

Hillfoots Woollen Industry

INTRODUCTION

The purpose in this section is to outline the historical background of the industry in relation to both economics and social conditions and also a number of other factors which acted together to direct the course of development.

For this purpose a large number of 'odds and ends' have been brought together from many disparate sources and, while far from being the whole story, it is hoped that a better overall picture may emerge from the piecing together of these different fragments in a coherent form.

To date there has been no comprehensive study made of the evolution of the economic structure of the woollen industry specifically in the Hillfoots area, however, a number of writers do touch on various factors which, at a national scale, affected the woollen trade generally. It would seem that the basis for such a study does exist (despite the fact that most of the mill records have disappeared) in that the Stirling Journal and Advertiser over many years in the 19th century carried a report on the state of the trade both in the local context and in relation to the market, national and international.*

It would be impossible to divorce a close consideration of the economics of the local trade from the social backdrop against which the evolution took place and with which it interacted. Particular reference may be made here to the dissertation by Robert McIntyre[1] (unpublished) which, though confined to Tillicoultry and dealing only with the period 1800 - 1861, is the most comprehensive examination of this area. McIntyre deals with population growth (causes and effects), numbers employed and conditions of work, educational facilities, political action and self-help societies and in so doing provides a useful insight into a way of life which we may reasonably assume was closely paralleled in the other Hillfoots towns, particularly Alva.

BACKGROUND UP TO THE 19th CENTURY

The origin of the woollen trade along the Hillfoots is not entirely clear, however, a number of writers (including Bremner in 1869 [2]) refer to evidence

---

* "Stirling Journal and Advertiser - a local index Vol.1. 1820-1869"
This booklet, prepared under a Job Creation scheme, provides an excellent tool for locating all references to the woollen industry during this period.

that woollen manufacture took place in the reign of Mary Queen of Scots in the mid-16th century when a reference to woollen goods appeared in the chartularies of Cambuskenneth Abbey (the Abbey owned most of the land along the foot of the Ochils). This is entirely possible since the woollen trade was certainly firmly established in the country.

A number of Flemish artisans had been gladly received by David I after having been driven from England in 1155 by Henry II who seemed to disagree with his predecessor's policy of actively encouraging the settlers. Whether or not it was at this time or, as Martindale[3] suggests, rather later in 1601 (when seven Flemish weavers were "induced" to settle in Scotland), that the continental methods of produding broadcloth and serges were introduced remains unclear. However, it is certain that in the early years of the 16th century wool production was becoming increasingly important. Turner[4] suggests that in the 15th and 16th centuries wool working was "...the most important of Scotland's industries " and made a considerable contribution to the export trade. The trade at that time followed the old-established pattern of exchange, principally with North Sea and Baltic markets.

From the middle of the 16th century onwards the Scots Parliament attempted to reduce exports of raw wool in order to encourage the expansion of native textile manufacture. This encouragement was further reinforced by the passing in 1597 of an act denouncing the import of English broadcloth which was said to be the chief cause of "...transporting of all gold and silver furth of this realm." (quoted by Martindale).

The Commission of Manufactures of 1597, by encouraging the woollen industry brought prosperity to the Scottish sheep farmers as well as to the manufacturers.

The material produced in the Hillfoots region during these early years, and indeed up until the end of the 18th century, was a coarse cloth commonly referred to by its now-famous name of Tillicoultry Serge and described in the Old Statistical Account[5] as "...a species of Shalom, having worsted warp and yarn warp.".

Despite the geographical proximity of the 2 towns of Alva and Tillicoultry there seems to have been some difference between the materials produced. It may well be that this difference was not in the actual quality of material but in the name attached to the cloth - Tillicoultry Serge. Whatever the case, it was said that ".... a serge web from Alva would not sell in the market while one from Tillicoultry remained unsold.". This definition gradually disappeared over the years as noted (and regretted) by Osborne in 1793 [5].

The practice of passing acts to encourage the trade continued and in 1641 an act intended to promote the production of fine cloth was introduced. Unfortunately the wool for such fine work had to be imported and though exempt from duty, and the final product exempt from tax, the trade eventually declined towards the end of the 17th century principally due to the lack of skilled workers and working capital. This development and decline had little effect on the Hillfoots villages where the fine wool trade had not been taken up to any degree.

Wool imports from England were prohibited in 1681, however, both that Act and the encouragement not to export raw wool were largely disregarded due to the conflict of interest between wool growers, manufacturers and cloth merchants in Scotland.

The Treaty of Union of 1707 had disastrous results generally in Scotland though the Hillfoots production of coarse materials felt comparatively little of the impact. English cloth could now be legally imported and the fine cloth manufacture, which had been on the decline at the end of the century in any case, ceased completely.

The 18th century saw the large-scale introduction and promotion by the state of linen manufacture in preference to wool. This was mainly due to the fact that England's fine woollens had crushed all remnants of parallel trade in Scotland immediately after 1707. There was however some assistance for wool working and a fund of £2000 per annum. was paid to Scotland in compensation for the hardship caused by the embargo on wool exports. This fund was administered by the Board of Trustees for Manufactures in Scotland set up in 1727. Unfortunately the Board did not greatly favour the woollen industry and in one year paid only £700 out of a total of £6000 for its encouragement. Patrick Lindsay*, one of the early presidents of the Board, laid great emphasis on the importance of linen as opposed to wool, However, he did concede that coarse woollen materials had a place.

The Alloa/Stirling/Hillfoots area continued in the production of serges and blankets and remained relatively unaffected by the upsurge in linen.(The same was true when cotton manufacture began on a large scale in Scotland.)

---

* Much of the work of Bremner was based on the writings of Patrick Lindsay (or Lindesay) and David Loch, referred to later.

The Board of Trustees continued to function throughout the 18th century and their reports indicate that they were not always in opposition to the woollen trade - indeed they were instructed to pay careful attention to it and in 1776 Loch*, who strongly advocated the development of woollen manufacture, reported a widespread and growing industry in Scotland.

By the late 18th century there was in Scotland a general dependence on supplies of wool from outwith the country, and even from Europe. However, in the Hillfoots/Alloa area the flocks on the Ochils continued to supply domestic manufacture. Following upon this general dearth of wool in Scotland greater attention was given to sheep rearing which resulted, toward the end of the century, in the setting up of manufactories for wool cloth at Inveraray and Haddington. The Board of Trustees noted this development and began to further encourage manufacturers by paying premiums for combing, spinning and dyeing and by awarding prizes. Despite this the 1790 report states that, "... the coarse woollen manufacture continued to gain ground only by slow degrees.".

Around the turn of the century spinning began to be mechanised with the introduction of hand jennies. From about 1815 onwards 'mule' spinning by power took the place of hand jennies and, since the power in these early days was from water, those areas which were already situated close to hill country and running water were well able to exploit this resource. The Hillfoots were favoured in this respect, being able to utilise the burns running from the Ochils into the River Devon. (The reasons for the location of the industry in the area and its continuance there are discussed in more detail below)

However, power-operated weaving looms did not become standard until well into the 19th century due mainly to technical problems, hence the increased output from the carding and spinning machines demanded an increased number of handloom weavers. It may be said here that most of these developments occurred initially in the Border counties, though carding machinery had been installed in Tillicoultry in the 1790's.

The slow progress of the coarse woollen trade at the end of the 18th century was slowed down further by competition from Bradford and the Hillfoots

---

* see footnote on previous page.

manufacturers in particular turned to the production of tartans, the serges, plaidings and blankets being gradually dropped over the early decades of the 19th century. Several of the weavers experimented with muslins in the early 1880's (Gibson[6]) however, this trade soon died out in the area*.

The increased demand for tartans and shawls was a direct consequence of the lifting of the ban on tartans in 1780 following the 1745 rebellion. This early period of the 19th century was of immense importance and saw a revolution in many spheres of the trade in the Hillfoots and, since most of the buildings still existing were built from this period onwards, we shall now consider in more detail these developments.

The close interdependance and mutual evolution of the Hillfoots towns, particularly Alva and Tillicoultry, requires that the area be looked at as a whole, however, reference will be made to individual developments in each place. The township of Menstrie has not been mentioned as yet, however, this was also an area in which the manufacture of serges, Scotch blankets and various other woollen goods was carried on though on a smaller scale.

As we shall see, the writer of the Old Statistical Account was far from being correct when he wrote in the 1790's that Tillicoultry would decrease in the number of its inhabitants and gave as two of his reasons the following: "the neglect of coal" and "the small attention and encouragement which is given to the weaving of Tillicoultry Serge.".

---

* The following extract from the Old Statistical Account indicates that muslins were introduced slightly earlier than suggested by Gibson:

   "Some of the weavers are now employed in making muslins; but as this branch is still in its infancy, it is impossible to say with what advantage it may be attended."

19th CENTURY ONWARDS

It is recorded in the Third Statistical Account[10] that the first half of the 19th century witnessed the transformation of Alva from a village into a manufacturing town. McIntyre, in dealing with the period 1800-1861 in Tillicoultry, makes the following point:
> "... it grew from a relatively small village community with a dying cottage-based woollen trade, into a bustling industrial town of some 5000 or more inhabitants."

It is evident therefore that this period was critical in the history of the area.

The factors which brought about this massive trade expansion in the 19th century are numerous and they combined together to form an entirely new context for the manufacture of woollen goods. Geographical location, trade outlets, availability of resources (raw material, labour, power, finance,etc.) and legislation are only a few of the aspects which it is hoped will emerge as we look in more detail at the development from 1800 onwards.

LOCATION   It is clear that the development of the Hillfoots settlements was related closely to the existence of the tributaries of the River Devon which flow down from the Ochils to the north through deep glens and spectacular gorges then across the flat land to the river itself. From medieval times these streams have been the very life-blood of the villages providing all domestic water and the driving power for the local flour or meal mill. One notable example was the mill (1642) above the hump-backed bridge in Menstrie drawings of which are now preserved by the Royal Commission on The Ancient and Historical Monuments of Scotland in Edinburgh.

More relevant to this study was the availability of the water for the process of wool production and this, combined with the sheep farming which took place on the Ochil Hills, was the basis for the growth of the cottage-based trade in coarse woollens. As already noted, the flocks on the Ochils continued to supply domestic manufacture at the end of the 18th century despite the shortage of wool elsewhere in the country and the subsequent necessity to import.

The water itself was pure and soft and clearly ideal for use in the pre-industrial process. However, it may well be wondered, if one visits the small streams today, how sufficient power was derived from them in order to drive the numerous water wheels, particularly during the summer months. We shall look later in more detail at the system at Tillicoultry, however it is interesting to note the observations of D.R. Macgregor[7] writing on the problems of land use and water supply in the Devon Valley.

Macgregor states that despite the steep gradient in the upper reaches of all the streams, the flow is remarkably maintained throughout the year probably due to "... the sponge-like effect of the boulder clay infilling the upper parts of the valleys and plastering the sides of the glens.". He notes that although the streams are in spate within 5 or 6 hours of the commencement of heavy rain, prolonged rain fails to produce a proportionate rise in the level of the streams. It would therefore appear that the Ochil streams possess a natural storage system which maintains flow. As we shall see, this natural storage system which allowed a reasonable flow throughout the year was supplemented at Tillicoultry by a system which gave storage for requirements on a daily basis.

The above observations of Macgregor were recorded in 1952, however, Gibson made the point in 1882 that the natural storage system had been lost. It is appropriate here to quote verbatim from his writings:

> "Tillicoultry burn, and the other streams of the Ochils utilized for water power, have been rendered of very much less value to the millowners than they used to be, from the extensive system of drainage that has been carried on for the last thirty years all over the Ochil range. Previous to this, the extensive morasses that exist on the hills used to act as natural reservoirs; and after a heavy rain, good full water was experienced for several weeks. Now, with the deep drains that intersect these places in all directions, the greater part of the water rushes off as fast as it falls, and in two or three days after a flood the streams are as small as ever. In consequence of this, the water-power of our burns has become of very little value indeed, and but for the aid of steam we would be helpless."

When we come to the industrialisation of the woollen trade the location becomes even more critical since the scope of demand on resources is extended. No longer are the ready supply of water and raw wool the main elements in assessing the viability of continuing in the manufacture of woollens. Factory space (or at least the availability of land at a reasonable price), low rents and skilled labour (those in the Hillfoots were already experienced in the woollen trade) were initially the factors which combined with those already mentioned to provide a framework for the introduction of the mill-based process. These being available, there were those prepared to invest capital to set the operation in motion. The close proximity to local coalfields ensured an abundant supply of coal to power the steam engines introduced at a later date - a further locational advantage.

These factors contributing to the growth of the industry and the population in the 19th century are mentioned by Macgregor and McIntyre and, in the case of the latter, are developed further. Particularly interesting is the suggestion advanced by McIntyre that the Hillfoots town of Dollar did not develop a dominant mill industry (as did all the others) due to the non-cooperation of heritors who may have wished to protect the town, with its prestigous educational establishment, MacNabb's School (now Dollar Academy), from the introduction of an industrial process and the associated mill buildings*. The assumption therefore is that cooperation was forthcoming from the heritors in the case of Menstrie, Alva and Tillicoultry.

The final advantage of location which we shall consider here was the geographical centrality of the Hillfoots in relation to the main trade centres. The Imperial Gazetteer of Scotland [8] (c.1852) notes that the markets for fabrics produced in Alva were Glasgow, Stirling, Perth and Edinburgh, Glasgow being the chief among these. It would be difficult to find a point more centrally situated in relation to these four outlets, even in isolation from a consideration of the other advantages noted above.

As an aside it is interesting to record that Martindale points out that, because communications in the 19th century were "....most readily directed towards Glasgow ", products in the Hillfoots were affected by this proximity to Glasgow merchants; ie. the development in the first half of the century of the manufacture of shawls, tartans and fancy materials was due, at least in part, to the type of trade with which Glasgow traders were generally concerned in the West of Scotland.

---

* The position of Dollar is discussed in more detail later.

TECHNOLOGY   As we have seen, the end of the 18th century seemed to mark an economic trough in the woollen trade generally and this is borne out, in relation to Tillicoultry at least, in that Osborne writing in 1793 states that only 21 weavers were resident in the Parish of Tillicoultry compared with 34 farmers. Bremner, writing in 1869, refers to the stamp master who, "....supposed that 7,000 ells of serge, and an equal quantity of plaiding, would cover the produce that passed through his hands annually from Tillicoultry." in the period from 1792 - 1795. He also notes that the woollen trade in Tillicoultry was in "...an almost lifeless state" from as early as 1755 until 1793.

However, the decline at Alva was not of the same proportions. The production of the traditional Tillicoultry Serge had slowly transferred to Alva as the Tillicoultry trade stagnated and eventually was concentrated almost entirely there. Blankets and serge remained the principal products of the mills in Alva until as late as 1829.

The installation of carding machines in Tillicoultry in the 1790's (Gulvin[9]) was the first step in a social and economic revolution in the area which increased the population of Tillicoultry from 909 in 1793 to 5054 in 1861. These early carding machines were hand-driven as evidenced in Gibson's record of the first carding engine in Tillicoultry :

> "It was driven by hand, and must have been quite as laborious an operation as the tread mill, but, of course, a decided step in advance of the little old hand cards."

Gibson also confirms the existence of a horse-driven carding engine in Alva which, he states, was seen in operation by a friend of his acquaintance.

Hand-driven jennies were introduced in the same period. It is recorded that, "...a jenny-spinner in the Hillfoots was reckoned to net about 9s. per week in the 1790's " (Gulvin).

From about 1815 onwards 'mule' spinning by power became general throughout the country and a system was set up in Tillicoultry to provide the required power to drive about 8 or 9 different water wheels (see section on water system at Tillicoultry). The Third Statistical Account[10] records that by about 1830 nine spinning mills were being driven by water wheels in Alva and from population statistics it can be seen that the expansion being witnessed at Tillicoultry as a direct result of mill building* was closely paralleled in Alva.

---

* This is the main thesis of McIntyre's dissertation.

It must be borne in mind that, as already mentioned, only the carding and spinning processes were powered in the first half of the 19th century. Powerlooms did not become commonplace until the 1850's, hence the weaving remained a cottage-based process, handloom weavers forming a large section of the industrial population up until about 1860.

As always in the process of mechanisation, there was a strong prejudice against the introduction of powerlooms and many of the male weavers refused to transfer their allegiance (and skills) to factory-based weaving[*]. As a result women were employed and in the 1851 Enumerator's Handbooks we find the first mention of 6 female powerloom weavers in Tillicoultry[**]. An indication of the subsequent rapid growth in the use of powerlooms is given in the following table, extracted from Gulvin :

CHANGES IN THE PRODUCTIVE CAPACITY OF THE HILLFOOTS, 1835-71

Year	No of mills	Per cent of total	No of spin'g spindles	Per cent of total	No of power looms	Per cent of total	No of workers	Per cent of total
1835							865	25
1838							1,410	28
1847							3,295	34
1850	45	25	72,095	32	38	16	3,669	38
1856	43	22	73,445	27	141	21	2,644	28
1861	38	21	71,261	22	278	21	2,297	23
1867	30	15	111,370	32	728	21	3,734	27
1871	33	15	143,516	34	715	7†	4,123	18

[County returns ceased in 1871; thereafter it is not possible to isolate the Hillfoot district for statistical purposes.]

†The large percentage fall in this year was the result of rapid expansion in the West of Scotland carpet industry.

Steam power, which came into use in the 1830's and 40's did not immediately overtake the use of water power, but instead was used to supplement it. As previously mentioned, readily available supplies of coal must have meant that steam engines in the Hillfoots area were able to run at a comparatively low cost in relation to those elsewhere in the country. Despite this, water wheels were still being installed in the late 1830's, notably at Craigfoot.

---

* Interestingly it is noted by Gibson that the womenfolk of an earlier period reacted similarly when waulk mills were first erected. Previously they had milled the blankets and plaidings by trampling them underfoot and were, "...rather jealous of the innovation.".

** Martindale's date of 1860 for the introduction of powerlooms to Tillicoultry seems to be somewhat late in relation to the evidence.

Bremner (1869) confirms that water and steam power were still being used in conjunction at that time to power the 37 carding engines in the 9 mills at Alva.

Little mention has been made of Menstrie so far, mainly due to the fact that relatively little material exists on the woollen mills there, nearly all of which have now disappeared. However, in relation to advancing technology it is recorded in the Report of the Factory Inquiry Commission* that John Archibald of Menstrie was utilising steam power as early as 1833. This appears to be the earliest reference to steam in the Hillfoots.

Self-acting spinning mules were yet another advance and one was purchased in 1939 from Mr Smith of Deanston to whom Bremner attributes the honour of being "inventor and maker". Gibson states that the "real inventor" was Richard Roberts of Wales. The mule was purchased by Messers R. Archibald & Sons of Tillicoultry in 1839 and was still in operation 30 years later according to Bremner.

THE TRADE   Returning to the trade itself, it will be remembered that Tillicoultry had declined to virtual stagnation and Alva had continued at a slow pace in the manufacture of serge and other coarse woollen goods.

According to Watson[11] (and confirmed by Wilson in the Imperial Gazetteer of Scotland c.1852), it was about 1821 that Tillicoultry manufacturers turned to the production of shawls, plaidings and tartans and later Alva followed this lead. The Imperial Gazetteer of Scotland records that tartan shawls were introduced in Alva in 1826 and soon became "....the most general article..."; "Chequered cassimeres were introduced in 1832, and speedily became prominent." The reason for the increased popularity of tartans was, as already mentioned, the lifting of the ban on the wearing of such material towards the end of the previous century.

The result of this change in direction, begun in 1821 and accelerated by the crisis in the trade of 1829, was basically the polarisation of the woollen textile industry. From 1825 onwards the Borders swiftly assumed the position of premier tweed district in Scotland and the Hillfoots area developed the growing interest in tartans to such an extent that it gained the reputation of being the prime supplier to the 'ladies end' of the fancy woollen market. Tartan shawls were particularly popular due,

---

* FACTORY INQUIRY COMMISSION Supplementary Report
Employment of Children in Factories. Part II (1834)
Irish University Press Reprints of British Parliamentary Papers.

Martindale suggests, to the interest expressed in the famous Paisley shawls a few years earlier at the turn of the century, and to the popularity of the tartan material itself.

As can be seen from the table on page 10, acceleration was rapid until the mid-19th century when the Hillfoots district possessed about 25% of Scotland's woollen mills and about 32% of its spinning capacity. Stillie[12] notes that the population increase was resultant upon the boom in tartans and states that during the period 1830-40 about 100 manufacturers were engaged in production. Around 1845-46 a ball was held at Alva to promote the wearing of tartan dress goods which by then had started to decline. By 1850 the situation had declined further and a period of depression in the trade was experienced. Gulvin and McIntyre cover in greater detail the causes of this decline, however, the basic reason was the unpredictability of the fashion trade, particularly at the 'ladies end', and again (as at the end of the 18th century) competition from Lancashire and Yorkshire for those markets which did still exist forced the Hillfoots into recession.

It may be that the period of 5 years depression (followed by revival in 1855-56) referred to by McIntyre is an over-estimation of the economic 'trough'. A report in the Stirling Journal and Advertiser of 18th February, 1853 reads :

> "The woollen manufactories, usually at a total standstill at this period of year, and for months thereafter, have had the whole of their machinery in full operation for some weeks ..... expecting continuous and large demand. Last year's demand from America has not yet been fully met."

The report of 11th March, 1853 is as follows :

> "....The emigration panic which prevailed among the operatives of the Hillfoots, a few months ago, has entirely vanished with the return of good trade and plenty work. The government has given notice that for the present weavers will not be sent out on the free emigration system; but this intimation seems quite superfluous. When the weavers are busy plying the spindle and the loom, the nuggets loose their magnetic charm in the imagination."

It would therefore appear that the times of crisis were around 1851-52 and possibly again in 1854-55. Stillie certainly suggests that the trade held on until at least 1855.

During the difficult period a number of the mill buildings were either offered for sale or rent and appeals were launched against the Assessor's valuation rate of "....7½% on the values of their Manufactories and machinery being fixed as the annual value of Manufactories and machinery.".* At the meeting of the Commissioners of Supply of Clackmannanshire on 15th September, 1855 a deputation was heard and thereafter the Commission fixed the rate at 5%.*

Recovery in the trade began in the late 1850's as evidenced by the following report from the Stirling Journal and Advertiser of 30th September, 1859 :

> TILLICOULTRY Never, we believe, within the last 30 years
> have matters been so brisk.....
> ....Messers J. & D. Paton have commenced
> building a large fine mill, close to their
> other factory, and also a series of large
> weaving shops.

Those who had previously produced shawls only, diverted their attention to the more stable men's trade and others experimented and broadened their scope of manufacture. The polarisation which had taken place in the Borders and the Hillfoots around 1830 was therefore reversed, the two areas becoming more interdependant, and more successful, from 1860 onwards.

In 1862 it was reported (3rd Statistical Account) that there were 10 woollen mills in Tillicoultry of which J.& D. Paton's was said to be the largest in Scotland. Trade continued relatively smoothly throughout the 1870's and 80's however, in 1890 the United States introduced the McKinlay Tariff at a rate of 49½% and later raised it to 57% in 1897. The industry had by this time become sensitive to conditions of international trade and this imposition came as a further crippling blow. Martindale suggests that this was probably the hardest blow ever suffered by the Scottish wool industry. The tariff virtually ended export to America,** therefore attention was redirected to Europe and recovery started once again only to be halted by the First World War. As in 1855 during a time of recession, the Hillfoots manufacturers in 1898 managed again to obtain a reduction in their assessments due to the state of the woollen trade (Gulvin).

---

* Commissioners of Supply of Clackmannanshire : minutes of meeting
   of 15th September, 1855. Central Region Archives. Ref. CC/1/1/5.

** Though modern writers suggest that the McKinlay tariff was the
    factor which ended export to America, Bremner mentions (in 1869)
    that exports to America had ceased, at least at that time :
> "....since the closing of the ports of the United States to our
> manufactured goods, trade has been limited to a few months of the year".

Clearly the records available relating to the 20th century would allow us to provide a far more detailed appraisal of the recent history of the industry in the Hillfoots district, however, for 2 reasons this is not being pursued here :

Firstly, the buildings themselves, which are the main subject of this report, were mostly constructed in the period which we have considered in some detail and this will suffice to provide an understanding of the context in which they were built. Any events which have subsequently taken place and which are relevant to, or particularly affected, specific buildings will be mentioned in the individual studies of these buildings.

Secondly, the period that has been covered is undoubtedly the most interesting and exciting in the history of the Hillfoots, at least as far as textile manufacture is concerned. The more recent history is comparatively uninteresting. It has, however, been suggested by Mr Bracewell (architect) that a lament should be written to the gradual decline in quality manufacture over the past 100-150 years. This may well be the subject for another study but will not be considered here !

Mill Buildings of the Past

This study is intended to deal principally with the mill buildings still in existence, however, it would seem that at least some attention should be given to those mills which were built in the early 19th century and which have since disappeared. Failure to make mention of them would leave a large gap in the general picture of development outlined so far and it is hoped that a consideration of the number of buildings which have gone will serve to highlight the importance, and perhaps the vulnerability, of those still remaining.

This section is therefore concerned with a summary of the mills in Menstrie, Alva, Tillicoultry and Dollar which are no longer with us. It is possible that there were others evidence of which has not come to light in this study.

MENSTRIE

In relation to its nearby neighbours, Alva and Tillicoultry, Menstrie receives little mention in the 19th century writings and the more recent references to the Hillfoots woollen industry. This is probably due to the fact that as a village it was much smaller than either of the others both before and after the 'boom' period of 1800-1860* (the comparative sizes of the villages in the 1860's can be seen in the extracts from the relevant Ordnance Survey maps of the period on pages 16, 17 and 18). Whether or not the following poem (included in the entry for Menstrie in the Imperial Gazetteer of Scotland) represents a widespread opinion of the village is unclear.

> Oh Alva woods are bonnie,
> Tillicoultry hills are fair,
> But when I think o' Menstrie,
> It maks my heart ay sair.

However, despite the bias of writers against Menstrie, conscious or otherwise, the village did have a role to play in the Hillfoots trade in that mills did exist there.

---

* Population according to Imperial Gazetteer of Scotland (c.1852) was 518 (117 houses).

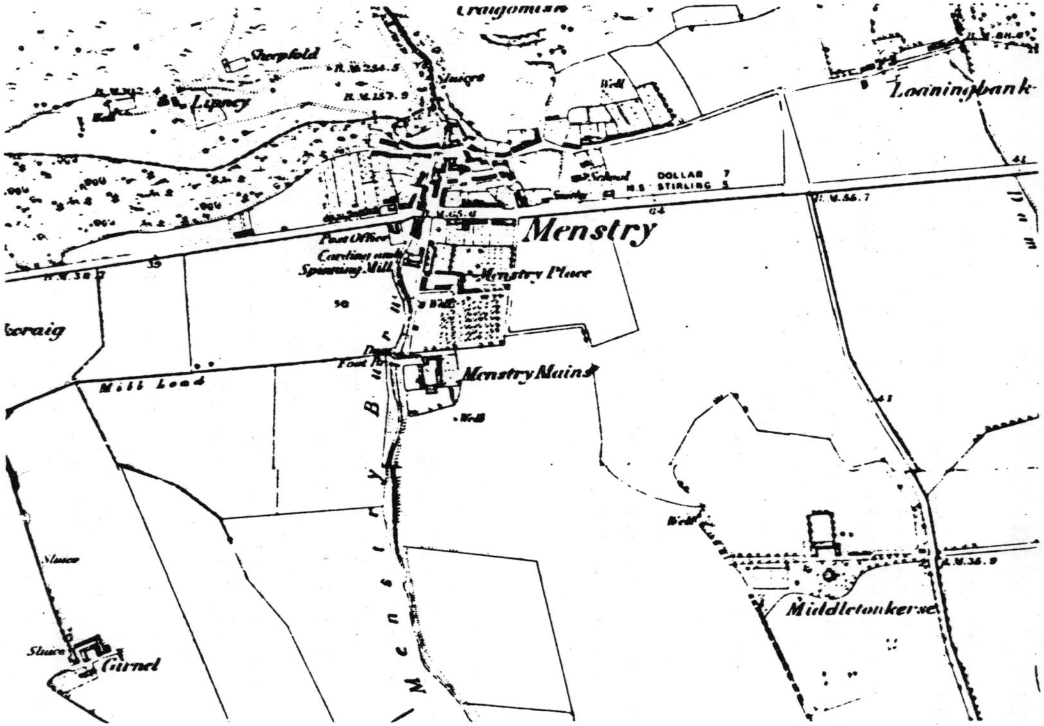

From Ordnance Survey map published 1866 from survey of 1862.

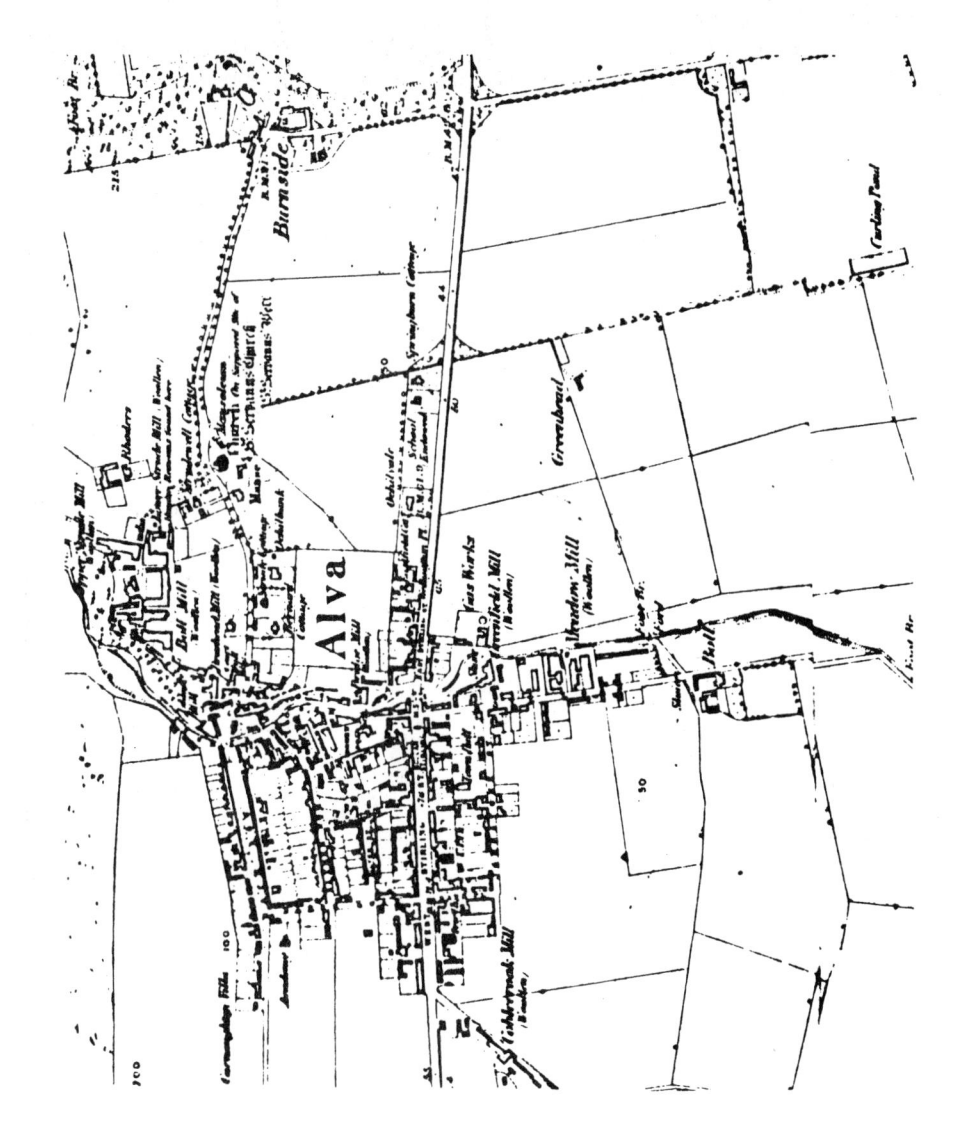

From Ordnance Survey map published 1866 from survey of 1862.

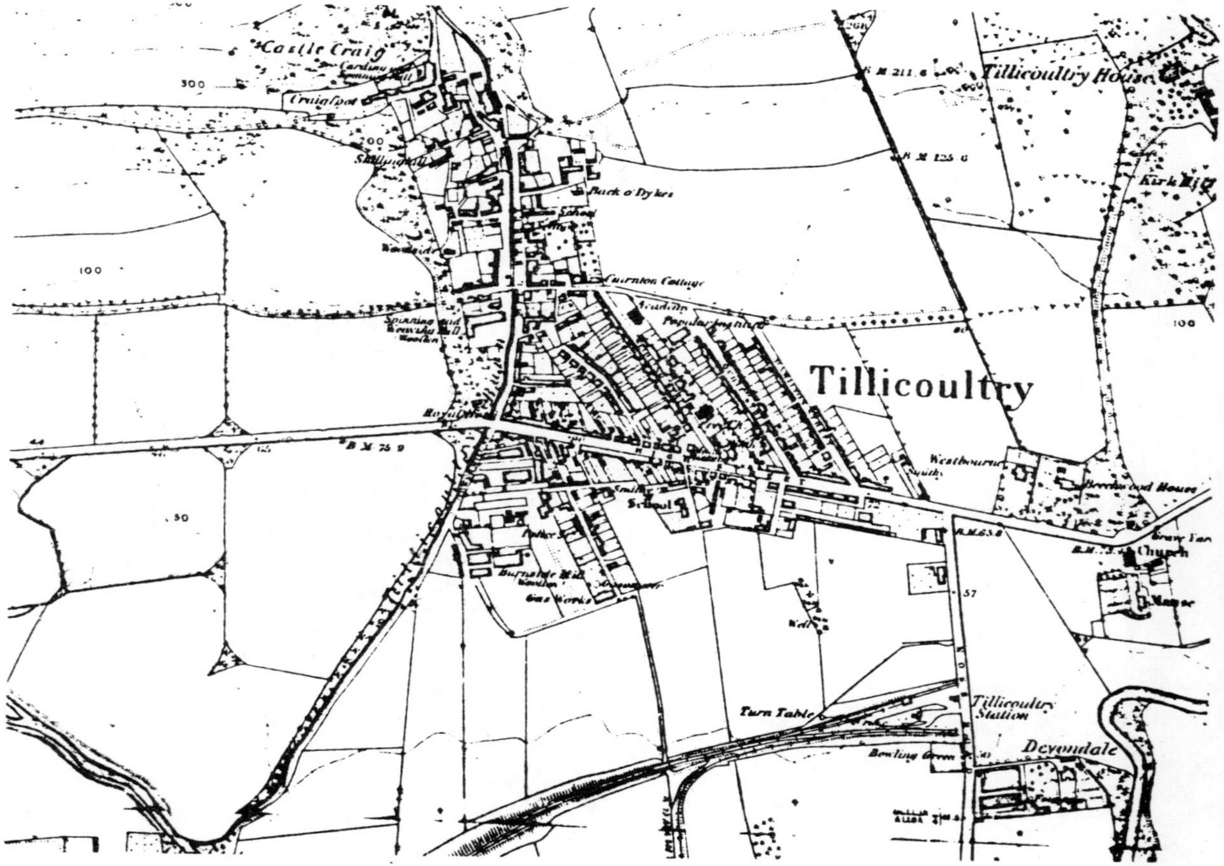

From Ordnance Survey map published 1866 from survey of 1862.

Archibald's Mill Up until the early 19th century woollen manufacture was carried on in a similar manner to that at Alva and Tillicoultry, however, around the turn of the century three brothers, later to become prominent in the trade, came from Tullibody and set up a small woollen mill in Menstrie. The three were John, William and Robert Archibald and the mill was that indicated as a 'Carding and Spinning Mill' on the east bank of the burn in the map on page 16.

William Archibald left Menstrie for Tillicoultry in 1806 to expand there as we shall see later. Robert followed him in 1817 leaving John Archibald to continue in Menstrie. John's sons, Andrew and Peter, continued operating in the mill at Menstrie long after their father's death.

From the answers supplied to the Factory Inquiry Commission in 1834 a great deal can be gleaned on the mill and more particularly, on the conditions of work. The following information is relevant here:

The west part of the mill was built in 1800 when the three brothers arrived from Tullibody and was subsequently extended to the east in 1810. The original part was a simple rectangular building of about 30' x 18' with thick walls made of large sandstone blocks from a local quarry. Erection was financed by the laird of Tullibody[*]. Immediately after building was complete the manufacture of yarns, blankets, etc. was commenced and by 1834 both steam and water power were employed (it will be remembered that this is the earliest record of steam power in the Hillfoots) with water providing, on average, half the power for the machinery. Latterly the mills were taken over by Messers. Robert Archibald & Sons, Tillicoultry, the head of the firm being one of the three original Archibald brothers. According to Mr Dawson of Menstrie, a horse-drawn lorry from Tillicoultry arrived every Friday with wool for the three spinning jennies.

Elmbank Mill As Gibson notes, little further development took place until 1864 when the first part of "...the very extensive and beautiful works" of Messers. Drummond and Johnston was constructed. It was at this time (rather than earlier as elsewhere) that Menstrie experienced its small 'boom', a large number of hands being required for the new mill. This was situated on the

---

[*] This information is contained in "Notes on the history of the Woollen Industry in the Hillfoots District" written by one A.G.P. from James Porteous and Co., Ltd. of Meadow Mill, Alva and now held in the 'history' file of Patons and Baldwins, Alloa.

west bank of the burn as indicated on page 21* and was known as the Elmbank Mill. Mr Dawson from Menstrie recalls that his mother worked half a day in the mill and half a day at school in 1886, and that the building was taken over in 1905 to be used for furniture manufacture. It can therefore be assumed that woollen manufacture ceased between these two dates, probably in the late 1890's when, as we have already seen, there was depression in the trade. The building which now remains and which is dealt with in Section 4 is of the typical mill type but was built at a later date than the old part which was demolished in the early 1970's. Being built in 1864, water power was never used as the driving force - Johnston and Drummond had their own gas retorts at the mill, the housings of which still remain.

Forthvale Mill   Another mill known as Forthvale Mill existed to the south of Archibald's Mill on the east bank of the burn, however, very little is known as to the history of this building. Its position is shown on the 1900 map on page 24.

ALVA

Burn Mill   Reference is made by William Drysdale,** in a paper read in Alva in 1886, to the Burn Mill in Alva built in 1801 and subsequently burned in 1810. He notes that from this incident the mill came to be known as the 'Burned Mill' and upheld its reputation by being burned several times more in the following years. It would appear from the paper that the mill was still in existence in 1886 though specific reference to it does not appear on the Ordnance Survey map of 1866.

Braehead Mill   According to Drysdale, Braehead Mill was constructed shortly after the Burn Mill though the building so identified by Hume[13] would appear to be of a much later period. It may well be that a reconstruction took place at some time, presumably after 1886. The reasons for this assumption are that the OS map of 1866 (page 17) identifies Braehead Mill, but not in its present plan form, and that Drysdale would probably have made reference to any rebuilding done before 1886.

In answer to the Factory Inquiry Commission of 1834, Wm. Drysdale & Sons stated that "....the principal erection was made in 1802, and an addition

---

* The reason for this building not appearing on the 1866 OS map is that the survey for that map was carried out in 1862.

** <u>Alva in the time of our Grandfathers</u> by William Drysdale. Reprint from the Alloa Circular of a paper read in Alva on 25th Jan.1886 at the opening of Norton School.

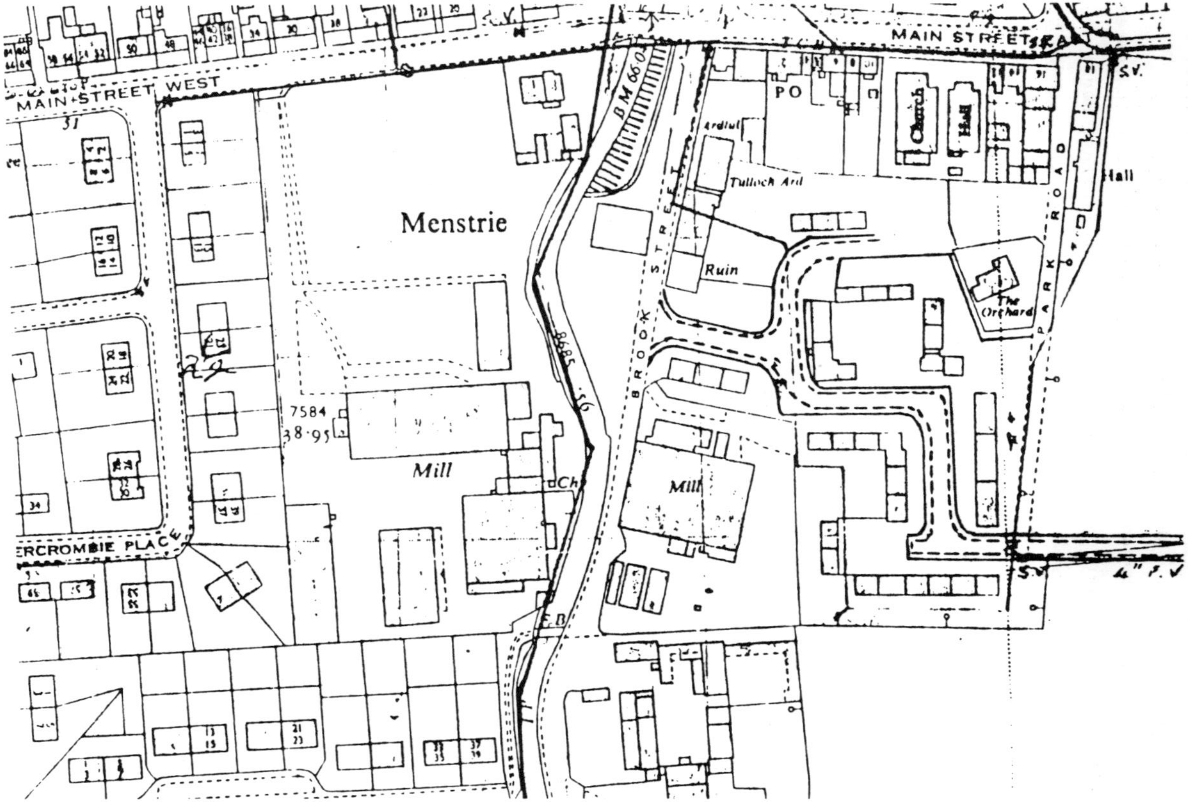

From 1960 Ordnance Survey map showing Elmbank Mills to the west of the burn and what was known as Forthvale Mill to the east. The rectangle between Brook Street and the burn represents the site of the old Archibald's Mill.

thereto was made in 1820." Braehead Mill was constructed by William Drysdale and, having noted that the mill was built shortly after 1801, it seems reasonable to assume that the building being referred to in this answer was indeed the Braehead Mill. If so, the information indicates that water provided the power and gave a regular output of eight horsepower or thereabouts.

Harrower's Mill   This was the next mill to be built though very little is known of it. Drysdale, in 1886, mentions that "...its capabilities for further usefulness seem departed.".

Horse Mill   This mill was situated close to the burn beside the lower bridge but had disappeared by 1886. No mill of this name appears on the map of 1866, however, one cannot therefore conclude that it had been demolished before this date since not every mill is identified by name, and in any case mills were so often labelled with different names at different times. For example, the 'Bridge Mill' on the 1866 map may well be the building later referred to as the Horse Mill.

As the title Horse Mill suggests, the power for the carding engine was provided by an old horse which was apparently regarded with some affection at the time. As we shall see, the association with the horse at Alva led to the residents of Tillicoultry applying the title 'Horse Mill Company' to the individuals who combined to build the Company Mill at Tillicoultry, several of them having been previously involved at the real Horse Mill at Alva.

Strude Mills   Though there remains a building called the Strude Mill, it is only part of what once was a large complex of buildings to the north of the town of Alva which was, in the estimation of Drysdale, built around 1827. The Ordnance Survey map of 1866 (page 17) gives some idea of the extent of the mills and identifies two individual buildings - the Upper Strude Mill and the Lower Strude Mill, none of which are the building which remains.

Cobblecrook Mill   This mill was built in 1838 by Mr John Scotland, the local miller, and was a 3-storey, 3-by-7 bay rubble structure. The stair was contained in a projecting semi-circular tower.

Whether or not the mill was ever used by the miller for his own trade is unclear, however, it would seem unlikely in view of its size. It is certainly referred to on the 1866 map as a woollen mill and also appears on a map of Clackmannan County of 1847-48[*]. Unlike the majority of the mills,

---

[*] Map of the County of Clackmannan as Politically Extended from actual survey during the years 1847-48. (Alloa Public Library)

Cobblecrook was not situated on the main burn running through the town, but to the west as can be seen on the map on page 17.

The mill was latterly owned by the Cobblecrook Dyeing Company Limited who came into being in 1855 in order to meet the needs of the weaving which up until that time was the sole process carried out at the mill.

In February 1974 the firm moved to new premises and unfortunately since then the Cobblecrook Mill has been demolished. Housing is currently being built on the site. However, it should be noted that the building demolished was not entirely original. After the war a new section was built around part of the old building which was then removed. An interesting beam engine also operated at Cobblecrook at one time.

<u>Meadow Mill</u>   This mill was built in 1839 (Drysdale) and was situated between the burn and what is now Brook Street. According to Drysdale the mill was commonly referred to as 'The Leviathan' due to its size and capacity. It was for many years under the ownership of the Porteous family* and closed early in 1964. The buildings have since been demolished and a new primary school built on the site.

Both spinning and weaving were carried on in the Meadow Mill buildings which comprised a 4-storey spinning mill (built of stone with a slated roof), a 2-storey weaving shop with powerloom and a single storey dyehouse**.
In this century James Porteous & Co.Ltd. dealt mainly in Angora and wool, breeding their own rabbits on the premises for the Angora.
A photograph of the mill itself and a number of the spinning mules (dating back to the 1860's) is included in Butt, Donnachie and Hume's book[14].
The O.S. maps of 1866 and 1901 indicate that considerable extension was carried out between the two dates. (1901 O.S. map on page 25)

<u>Mill at Brook Street</u>   Until relatively recently a mill building stood at the corner of Brook Street and East Stirling Street in Alva. Little detail is now available, however, it is known that oak pillars rather than cast iron columns were used in this building suggesting that it was one of the earliest mills in the town. Records show that it also had a pantile roof which would bear out this assumption. At one time the premises were occupied by Wilson Brothers from Glentana Mills (or Dalmore Works as they were then known).

---

* The records of James Porteous & Co., Woollen Manufacturers, Alva. are held by the Economic History department of Strathclyde University and may be consulted through the National Register of Archives (Scotland).

** A handloom weaving shop with 6 looms was also included ; C.B.A. record cards (copies) - Royal Commission on Ancient and Historical Monuments.

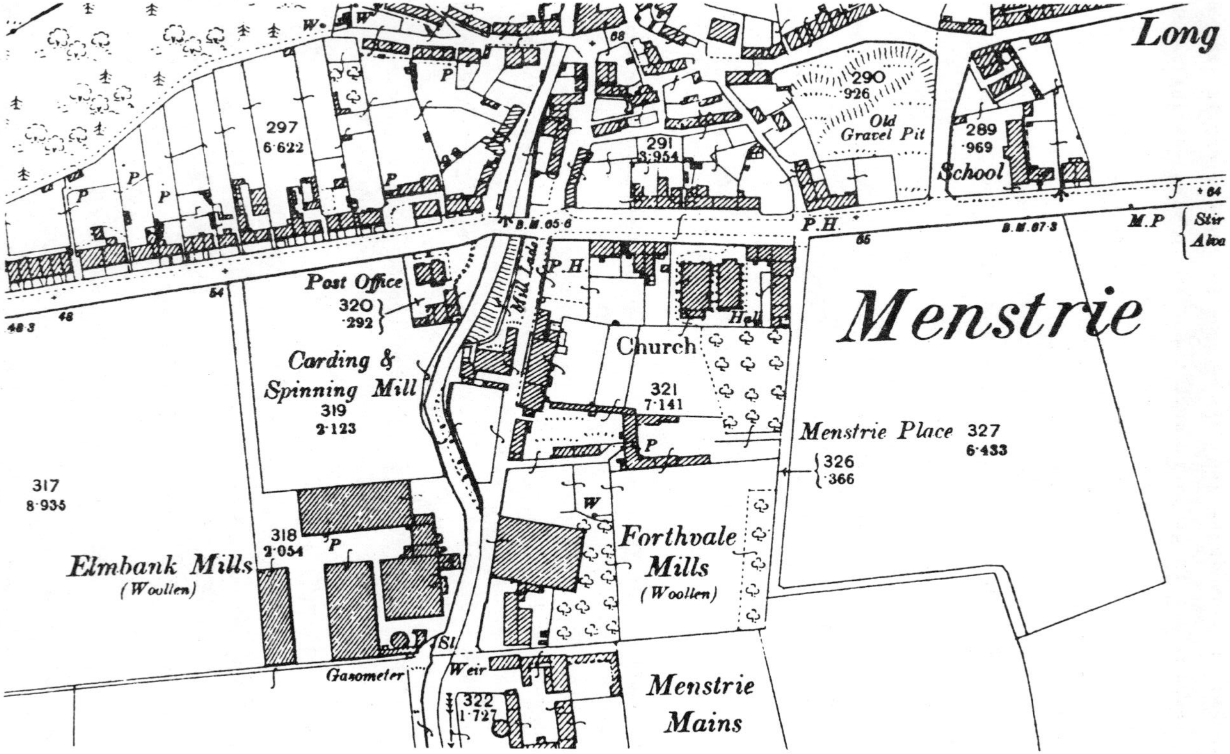

From Ordnance Survey map published in 1900.

From Ordnance Survey map published in 1901.

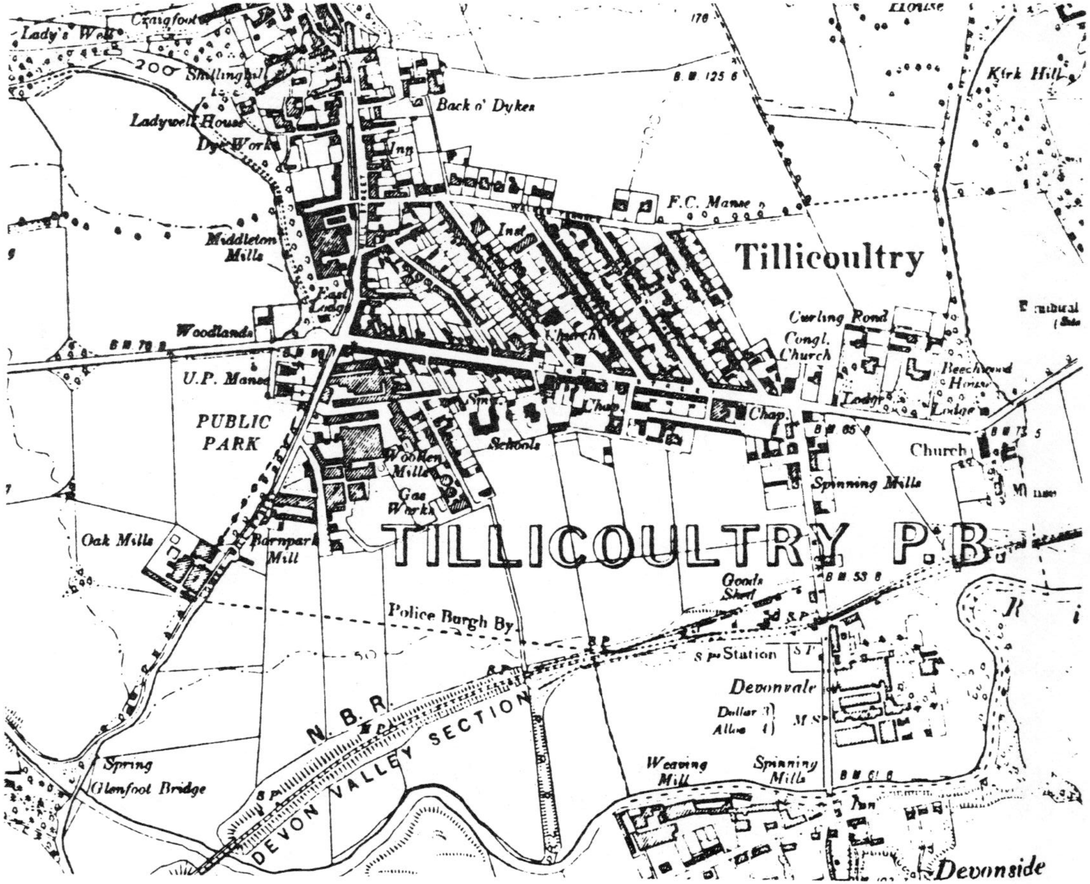

TILLICOULTRY. From Ordnance Survey map published in 1901.

Brookfield Mills   Brookfield Mills were located to the south-east of the present Ochilvale Mills as can be seen on the O.S. map of 1901 (page 25). These spinning mills were erected in 1865 by Mr William Ross who founded the prosperous business of Messers. William Ross & Sons in 1838 and who played a prominent part in developments in the mid-19th century.

It is recalled by Mr Sinclair (sen) of the Clock Mill in Tillicoultry that at one time the premises at Brookfield were concerned with the specialised field of tapestries.

Other Mills   A number of other mills which no longer exist are shown on the Ordnance Survey maps, notably the Boll Mill situated below the Strude Mills on the 1866 map and designated a woollen mill. It would appear reasonable to assume that this building was one of the three in Alva owned by the Drysdales and referred to in the returns of W. Drysdale jun. to the Factory Inquiry Commission of 1834. The reason for this assumption is that the following article links the Drysdales with a mill referred to as the 'Bole Mill'.

> "We are sorry to say that intelligence has reached town that the Bole Mill at Alva was yesterday destroyed by fire. The property belongs to Messers. Drysdale and we regret to add that the loss sustained has been calculated at no less than from £3000 to £4000, though we sincerely hope that this report may prove to be greatly exaggerated."
>
> Stirling Journal & Advertiser.
> 9th October, 1856.

The returns to the Commission indicate that of the three mills one was built in 1802 (Braehead), one in 1827 and one about 1794-95. The Imperial Gazetteer of Scotland confirms that the first woollen factory was built before the turn of the century, though the date given is slightly later (1798). Whether or not the Boll or Bole Mill was the 1827 building or the earlier one is not clear. Whatever the case, all three mills were water-driven in 1834, the 1827 and the 1790's building both being of about 10 horsepower. Gibson notes that a fine weaving shop was added in 1845.

The Commission also received returns from John Archibald, Alva referring to his works, erected in 1825-26 and employed in the production of woollen yarns for shawls. Here again water power drove the machinery with a regular output of five horsepower. The siting of this mill is not known nor is the position of the premises of James Harrower whose mill was built in 1807 and was producing blankets, plaidings and worsted shawls as well as housing a dyeing process. Water again provided the motive force. Harrower was one of those who collaborated later to build the Company Mill in Tillicoultry (see below).

The Third Statistical Account records that by 1830, a total of nine spinning mills were being driven by water wheels in Alva.

TILLICOULTRY

With the help of references and relevant maps of the period it is possible to identify 20 distinct mill buildings which were built in Tillicoultry in and around the 19th century. A number of these buildings still exist, in part or in whole, and are dealt with in more detail in Section 4. However, the following gives a brief summary of the available background history to the buildings which have not survived to the present day.

Waulk Mill It is stated by Gibson that the first mill was a waulk mill erected at the end of the 18th century by one Thomas Harrower. No records exist which would indicate the size, or even the location of the building, however in the returns by Robert and William Archibald to the Factory Inquiry Commission dated 23rd May 1833, they state that the premises occupied by themselves were originally used as a waulk mill in 1796 (see Middletoun Mill).

Castle Mills (old mill) Just prior to 1800 the three Christie brothers, John, Duncan and William built the first spinning mill with a waulk mill attached in Tillicoultry on the west bank of the burn to the north of what is now the Clock Mill. In 1817-18 the mill was taken over by Robert Walker and remained in the Walker family for many years. It was latterly used only as a store with handloom weaving still taking place in the attic. The mill is illustrated in the print from Gibson's book (reproduced on page 29) though the degree of flexibility which 'artists licence' afforded at the time of drawing must be borne in mind.

Middletoun Mill Expansion in business forced the Christies to seek new premises and they built the Middletoun or middle-of-the-town mill further down the Tillicoultry burn still on the west side. According to a drawing of the property belonging to Robert Archibald & Sons dated November 1922[*],

---

[*] This map is held by Mr Bowie, Chief Engineer. Interbobbin (UK) Ltd. Middleton Mills, Tillicoultry.

CASTLE MILL

CRAIGFOOT MILL

Having, for business purposes, got views taken of both our works, I herewith insert them; and they will give a better idea than any description can give of what some of the first mills in Tillicoultry are like. The mill in the foreground of the view of Craigfoot Mill is Dawson's Mill, which we only lease; while the large mill at the foot of the Craig is the one built by J. & R. Archibald in 1838; and the wing behind it (increased in height when the big mill was built), by Mr. William Archibald, their father, in 1806.

The one-storied building below the entrance gate (in the view of Castle Mill) is the upper end of the first mill in Tillicoultry, built by the Messrs. Christie in the end of last century. The large mill is the one built by Mr. Andrew Walker; while the dwelling-house is on the site of the old Castle, formerly referred to, and from which the works got their name. The roof of a house in the foreground of this view (on the opposite side of the street from the entrance gate) is the roof of The Horse, or Company Mill.

29

Extract from Gibson's Book showing some of the mills which have now disappeared.

this mill (referred to as No.2 Mill) was of three storeys with an attic. This is borne out by the photograph of 1877 (page 31) on which the building can be seen at the left-hand side. The characteristic shape of the wheel housing can be seen in this photograph on the south face of the mill. The 1922 drawing indicates that water from the lade approached the wheel at right angles, presumably dropping onto it to provide power.

One of the Christie brothers (John) died and the other two emigrated around 1817 when the building was bought by Robert Archibald (who had already been involved for about 18 years with the mill at Menstrie). Additions were subsequently made in 1821 and in 1826. According to Archibald, writing in 1833[*], water supply was plentiful for 8 months in the year and seven horsepower could be derived from it during this period. At times when water was more scarce he estimated that only four horsepower was available.

In 1836 Robert Archibald & Sons (the firm formed by Robert and his 4 sons) built new premises (the present Middleton Mills) and removed to them, however, they retained ownership of Middletoun Mill, James Monteith and Alexander Drysdale becoming tenants. According to Gibson the building was known in the latter half of the 19th century as the Old Mill of Robert Archibald & Sons works. This is borne out by the entry against Robert Archibald & Sons, Manufacturers in the draft valuation for the County of Clackmannan[**]; the 'Description of Subject' is, "Woollen mills in Tillicoultry, old and new."

Craigfoot Mill The third mill to be built in Tillicoultry was the Craigfoot Mill built around 1806 by William Archibald who, like his brother, had originally started in the woollen trade at Menstrie. The mill was built well to the west of the Tillicoultry burn and at a much higher level (see 1866 and 1901 O.S. maps) and when the time came to employ water power, the location necessitated an elaborate arrangement of supply by means of a timber aqueduct (see Section 3). Subsequent on William Archibald's death in 1826 the building became known as the Widow's Mill, Archibald's wife having elected to carry on the business.

In 1838 a new building was erected alongside the existing Craigfoot Mill and incorporated into this building was a massive iron water wheel drawing

---

* Factory Inquiry Commission Returns.

** Draft Valuation for County of Clackmannan 1855-56 held by Central Region Archives (Ref. CC4/2/1)

Devastation caused by the flooding of Tillicoultry Burn on 28th August 1877.

its supply from the aqueduct. An indication of the scale of the wheel is given in the drawing on page 33 by Bracewell, Harrison & Coton (architects) which shows the mill as viewed from the east. The 1838 building is on the left. The mill is also shown in the drawing on page 29 and here the original building can be seen behind the main block though it too was altered in 1838, an additional storey being added.

The year following this expansion the mill was taken over by John and Robert Archibald, William's two sons, who formed the company of J.& R. Archibald and who were later responsible for the large Devonvale Mill. In 1857 Mr Archibald of Devonvale and William Gibson entered into partnership. By this time Devonvale was fully operational and Gibson moved from Dawson's Mill (see below) to Craigfoot. Gibson gives an interesting account of fires at the 'big mill' (presumably Craigfoot) in March 1858, July 1863 and November 1876.

There are still those alive who remember the giant iron wheel in operation in the 1920's when as children they dared to peer through the large timber doors on the east side of the mill. The building was demolished in the 1930's.

Company Mill   The Company Mill was built by the "..eight or nine gentlemen" connected with the Horse Mill in Alva who formed James Balfour & Co. Unlike the majority of other mill owners who formed family businesses, James Balfour & Co. was simply a consortium of business colleagues with no close family links, as is evidenced by Gibson's list of 6 of the partners[*].

The mill was built (c.1812) to the east of the site of the Castle Mills and changed hands at least three times before coming into the ownership of Robert Archibald & Sons some time after the 1880's. The 1922 drawing shows the Company Mill as a 2-storey building with a wheel situated east-west at the north end. This was served by the water system discussed in more detail in the next section. The building appears in the foreground of the drawing on page 29 . Apparently this building came to be known as the 'Cuddy Mill' and is referred to as such in the minutes of the meeting of The Commissioners of Supply of Clackmannanshire (15th September, 1855)

Dawson's Mill   Dawson's Mill was erected in 1821[**] by one James Dawson and was situated immediately to the south-east of Craigfoot Mill. It was later incorporated into the water power system .

---

[*]   James Balfour,; James Ritchie; James Morrison; David Drysdale; William Rennie; John Cairns.

[**] This is the date given by James Dawson himself in his returns to the Factory Inquiry Commission in 1833. Gibson's date of 1811-12 would appear to be wrong.

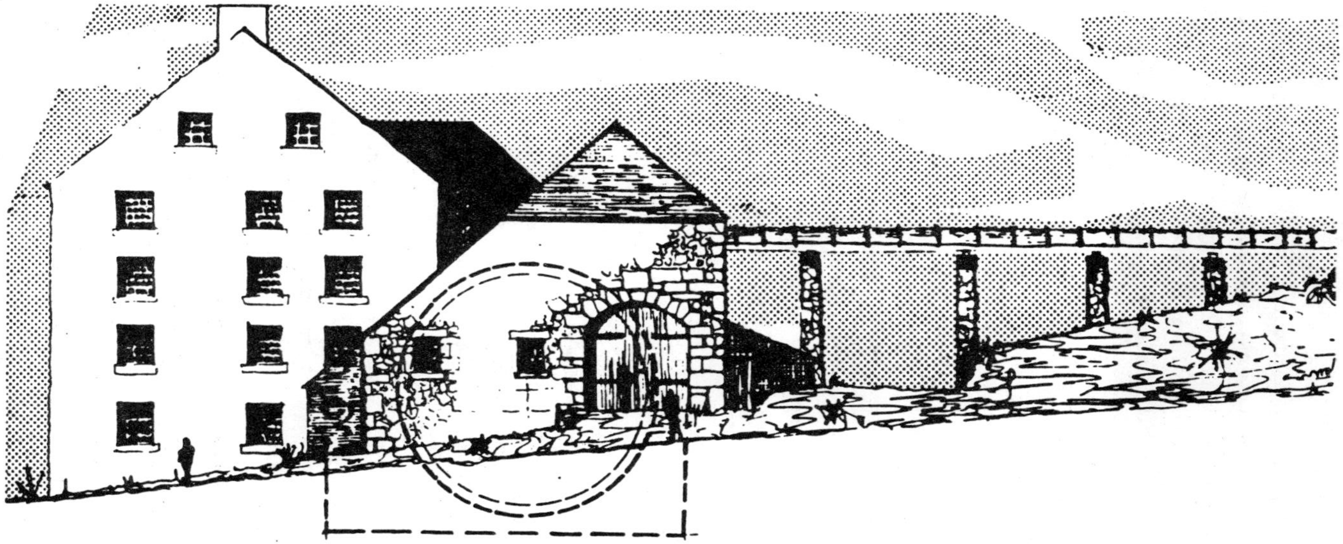

LADE AND WHEEL AT MILL NEAR QUARRY. (CRAIGFOOT MILL)
THE LARGE IRON WHEEL WAS WORKING IN 1925.

From Bracewell, Harrison & Coton drawing of water system at Tillicoultry.

In the early 1840's the mill passed into the hands of a John Cairns[*] and was subsequently leased, the north part to J.& R.Archibald as a weaving shop, and the south part jointly to J.& D.Paton and J.& R.Archibald.
In 1848 William Gibson leased the whole mill and continued carding, spinning and weaving independantly until 1851 when he joined in partnership with Robert Archibald of J.& R.Archibald . Work was then moved to Craigfoot, though the partnership (William Gibson & Co.) retained the the tenancy of Dawson's Mill until at least 1880.

Again this building can be seen in the drawing on page 29. It was also referred to as the Old Mill, for example on the 1922 drawing of property belonging to Robert Archibald and Sons.

New Castle Mill (or Andrew Walker's Mill or Hutcheson's Mill)   As already noted, Robert Walker acquired the Old Castle Mill around 1817. His two eldest sons built what is now known as the Clock Mill (see Section 4), however, his younger son Andrew also followed their example and built the New Castle Mill to the north-east of the Old Castle Mill and immediately adjacent to the west side of the burn. The building was erected some time after 1820 and had its own gas works which also provided a supply to the village of Westertoun[**].

The business was carried on after Andrew's death in 1843 by his widow and following her withdrawal in 1849, changed hands a number of times before being purchased by William Gibson & Co. in 1877 following the death of the owner at that time, Mr Hutcheson. Mr Hutcheson was drowned in the great flood of that year.

A reference to the 'Sparrow Mill' appears in certain documents and according to Mr Sinclair (sen.) it is most likely that this was the mill referred to since the Sparrow Road at one time ran alongside it.
The mill can be seen in the drawing on page 29.

Henderson's Mill   (later known as the 'Burnt Mill')   This building was erected later than those already mentioned in 1830 by a Mr John Henderson who made use of the water from the Ladies' Well for his steam engine. The Ladies' Well was situated at some distance to the west of the burn,

---

[*] The Collection Books for 1840 indicate that "...John Cairns and others" occupied premises as a woollen manufactory somewhere in the village at that time which would lead us to assume that this was the same John Cairns who was part of the consortium which set up the Company Mill.

[**] Westertoun was one of the three small villages which originally made up the parish of Tillicoultry and was centered around the Tillicoultry burn. The other villages were Eastertoun and Coalsnaughton.

and clearly, therefore, water power was never utilised here. In 1839 the 3-storey building was destroyed by fire, though the shell remained in its ruinous state for another 35 years, hence the name 'Burnt Mill'.* The mill was restored to form a dyehouse in 1874. Its location as such can be seen from the 1901 O.S. map on page 26.

Gibson states that Mr Alexander Robertson (who occupied one of the floors of Henderson's Mill) was completely ruined by the fire of 1839 due to the fact that he was not insured. It may be surmised that Mr Henderson also found himself in a difficult position; in the Collection Books for 1840 the following pencilled note appears against the name of John Henderson : "...in arrears but paid on 1st February, 1841 by J. Johnstone.". Johnstone was the local landowner.

Marshall's Mill   Marshall's Mill was built around 1836 and relatively few references to this building exist, however, we do know that after a period of 10 years, the mill was sold to Messers. Paton following Robert Marshall's failure in business. The building was incorporated into Paton's works which are considered in more detail in Section 4.

Spinning Mill   A very brief reference is made by Gibson to a mill erected for spinning in 1864 by Edward Senior & Co., however, no details of its size or location have come to light.

Mills at Devonside

Monteath's Mill   This was built in 1834 by a Mr Thomas Monteath and was occupied by himself and his son William who formed the company of Thomas Monteath and Son. The erection of this first mill on the banks of the River Devon was the basis for the development of the small village of Devonside.

Unfortunately very little information remains which would allow us to pinpoint accurately the position of this mill, however, Gibson, writing in 1882 does state that it was, "...the second one from the bridge.".

The mill adjacent to the bridge (referred to by McIntyre as the Bridge Mill) was built 2 years later by a partnership of three - James Henderson, David Moir and Robert Walker. Another mill was built in 1836 by a partnership of five and was located to the west of Monteath's Mill and again in 1841 yet another was erected by a partnership, this time

---

* It will be remembered that a similar title (The Burned Mill) attached to a mill in Alva under similar circumstances.

of four. This mill was located further to the west along the bank of the River Devon. Both of these mills were bought by Alexander Drysdale in 1849 and he extended by building a new spinning mill with a large powerloom shed.

Farthest west of all was what Gibson refers to as a weaving factory erected around 1845 by Messers James and Matthew Thomson. An article in the Stirling Journal and Advertiser of 15th July, 1859 refers to the burning, "..12 months ago..." of a large, 3-storey woollen mill at Devonside. The report states that the wool store, saved in the previous blaze, had now itself been destroyed by fire and that the whole building, including the mill, now stood gutted. Whether or not this building was the property belonging to Messers Thomson is unclear. The Stirling Journal and Advertiser of 5th November, 1858 refers to a recent fire at the premises of Messers Thomson which would tie in with the above report, however, the property referred to in this report is in Alloa.

Whatever the case, the draft valuation for 1855-56 (see footnote on page 30 for reference) does indicate that James Thomson did occupy half of a mill at Devonside at that time, the other half being occupied by one Alexander Izatt from Dollar.

Related Buildings

In addition to these mill buildings, the draft valuation of 1855-56 reveals that a number of loomshops existed, normally adjacent to a house. It is likely that loomshops had existed for many years before 1846 - the first time that records of them appear in the Parish Collection Book. McIntyre deals in some depth with this possibility. Even the records which do exist probably cover only a small percentage of the buildings within which weaving took place. Bremner, writing in 1869, indicates that 9 loomshops existed in Tillicoultry containing 180 looms, this being in addition to the mills themselves. Handloom weavers rented a 'stance' in such a loomshop, though most had their own looms.**

Gibson also refers to the finishing works of Mr Robert Drysdale erected in 1860, however the precise nature or location of this building is not known. "Comodious premises" were erected in Moss Road by Mr Robert Young in 1860 but once again references do not indicate what type of building this was.

** Interesting details of wage rates, conditions, etc. are contained in Reports from Assistant Hand-Loom Weavers' Commissioners (1839) contained within the Irish University Press reprints of Parliamentary Papers.

DOLLAR

As is suggested elsewhere, the failure of the town of Dollar to develop as a major centre for the woollen trade in the 19th century may well have been due to the reluctance of local heritors to encourage such an industry in close proximity to the prestigous MacNabb's School. Certainly the other locational advantages discussed in Section 1 were similar at Dollar. Further weight may be added to this argument in that there exists drawings dated 1836 by one James Home showing the layout of 15 proposed mill sites in Dollar*. These mills are laid out in a crescent form to the east side of the Dollar burn and step progressively downhill. The drawings indicate that a damhead and reservoir were proposed from which an aqueduct would channel water to the upper mill. Water would then flow downwards driving all the mills in the crescent form.

The map of 1866 shows a woollen mill situated to the west side of the Dollar burn and we know from the Factory Inquiry Commission of 1834, and the 1840 Collection Books for Dollar Parish, that the Drysdales of Alva did operate a water-driven mill at Dollar. This building was erected about 1818. The date of 1820 given by Maurice Lindsay for the demolition of the mill is not borne out by the evidence (see article in SCOTTISH FIELD; March 1976).

The New Statistical Account indicates that the woollen mill employed only 2 men, 4 boys and girls, hence was relatively small. Wool was brought on horseback across the Ochils from Blackford. The following notice from the Stirling Journal and Advertiser of 25th February, 1859 refers to a Wool Mill at Dollar though whether or not this was the same building is not certain. However, only one woollen mill is indicated on the map of 1866.

> Adjourned Sale of the Wool Mill in Dollar at the reduced upset price of £400.
> Golden Lion Hotel, Stirling. 4th March, 1859 at 1.00 pm.
> All and whole the piece of ground, houses and gardens in Burnside of Dollar, which sometime belonged to the late Robert Pitcain, with the SPINNING MILL erected thereon, Water Wheel, Great Gearing, Machinery and Utensils.

Whatever the case, the building or buildings are long since gone and no trace remains in Dollar of the woollen trade of an earlier age. Dollar was better known for its bleachfields, begun in 1787 and which extended to 30 acres at one point**. At that time they were principally for the bleaching of linen goods though the First Statistical Account notes that much of the material bleached at that time was cotton.

---

* Register House Plans Collection, Scottish Record Office, West Register House, Edinburgh. RHP 1235/1 1235/2 1236/1

** New Statistical Account.

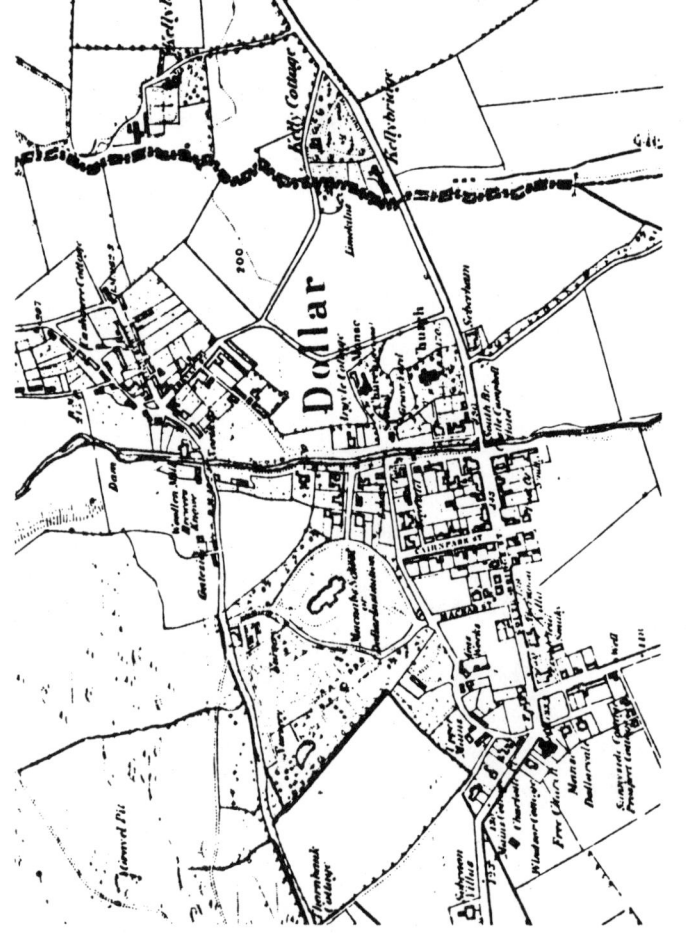

From Ordnance Survey map published 1866 from 1862 survey.

Water Power System at Tillicoultry

The water power system at Tillicoultry has already been mentioned in passing. Here we shall look in more detail at this system, one which was rather more complex than the relatively straightforward arrangement at Alva and elsewhere where wheels were driven either directly by the burn or by mill lades simply diverted from the burn.

Craigfoot Mill had been built by Robert Archibald (c.1806) well away from the Tillicoultry burn and hence, when water became a necessity, the diversion of water to his premises became a large and expensive undertaking. Not only was the building set well back from the water, but it was also many feet above the level of the burn at its closest point.

Gibson, writing in 1882, records that the original damhead was erected in 1824 (there is some doubt as to the precise date - 1826 is suggested elsewhere) and was situated a little above the quarry. This obviously gave a reservoir of water which Archibald then utilised as a 'take-off' point and from which he constructed a timber lade running at high level to his Craigfoot Mill. This lade or aqueduct (referred to as such in the O.S. map of 1901) was of considerable length and was, at one point at least, 20 feet deep. It formed the basis for the evolution of the system which can be traced on the drawing by Bracewell, Harrison & Coton which is included as an appendix to this report. Remains of the massive stone piers which once supported the structure may still be seen to the west of the road running to the quarry (see page 40).

As can be seen from the drawing, the lade was directed into the wheelhouse at Craigfoot and overshot the massive iron wheel. This 'overshot' wheel system was reckoned to be the most efficient method of utilising the available water, assuming that it approached the wheel at a high enough level. Mr Sinclair (sen.) of the Clock Mill well remembers the dangerous practice in the 1920's of wading along this lade and peering down onto the wheel from above. Latterly at Craigfoot supplementary power was provided by a gas engine acting with a governor to give additional power as required.

Returning to the dam itself, it is well documented that, not long after its construction, the womenfolk of the village proceeded to demolish the damhead with axes and hammers. The cause of this minor uprising was that Archibald discharged the effluent from his waulk mill into the village burn, there being no other form of sewer at the time. The night following its destruction the dam

Remains of stone piers which once supported timber aqueduct above Craigfoot Mill.

was quickly rebuilt in order to allow operations at the mill to continue uninterupted. Once again the women set about their destructive work on the new erection. At this point it became necessary to construct a sewer and so the conflict ended. The damhead was rebuilt and was allowed to remain until about 1857 when a new one was required. The location for the new dam was further up the glen and the remains of the timber dam can still be seen in this position (see following pages). The drawing of the water system also includes an illustration of the dam itself (see appendix).

From Craigfoot the water continued down to Dawson's Mill and passed through driving a wheel running in an east-west direction. It may be assumed that the wheel was located in line with the large arched opening which can be seen in the drawing of Dawson's Mill on page 29. The end of the timber aqueduct at a higher level can also be seen on this drawing. The ruins of the east facade of Dawson's Mill may still be seen (page 44).

It was thought by some that there were at one time two wheels in Dawson's Mill, however, it is more likely that the additional water course acted only as a bypass. Certainly Gibson, replying to the Factory Inquiry Commission in 1833, states that there is "A water wheel of about seven or eight horsepower". As we shall see, the practice of providing a bypass was used throughout the system, this being one of the features which gives it interest.

From Dawson's Mill the water was directed to the Company Mill or what was later known as the Cuddy Mill. The 1922 drawing of the property belonging to Robert Archibald and Sons indicates that the mill race approached the Company Mill from the north-west and was then passed through the north end of the building driving a wheel running east-west.

From here the lade crossed to what is now a grassed area. The 1922 drawing indicates a "Pit" here (this is shown by a small rectangle on Bracewell, Harrison & Coton's drawing). Mr Sinclair recalls seeing mountings for a water wheel in this pit and it would seem likely that the wheel was connected with the New Castle Mill (also referred to as Andrew Walker's Mill and Hutcheson's Mill). The reproduction from Gibson's book on page 29 shows what is probably the wheelhouse on the north-west corner of the main building.

Following the lade down we now come to a complicated arrangement of sluices. At this point there was another intake from the burn which could be controlled and was used for 'topping up' the system. There was also an

Remains of timber dam above Tillicoultry.

Operating mechanism - dam at Tillicoultry.

Remains of east facade of Dawson's Mill.

overflow from this point back into the burn as can be seen from the drawing. The lade then diverted down to the west side of the Clock Mill but could be shut off allowing the water to flow directly into the burn via the overflow. This allowed the Clock Mill wheel to be 'run dry' for maintenance. A channel running down the west side of the building directed the water onto the top of the wheel. The remains of this part of the system and the position of the water wheel can still be seen (see page 46 and photographs in Section 4).

To the south of the Clock Mill there was another intake from the burn which allowed the Middletoun or middle-of-the-town mill to be operated even when the Clock Mill was out of action and vice versa. This section of the 1922 drawing is reproduced on page 47 since it illustrates an interesting link-up between these two mills. Both were water-driven but were also connected by an underground shaft of 6" or 7" diameter with which was associated a small engine (engine house). This acted as a governor between the two mills, coming into operation as required to top up the power available from the flow of water.

The wheel at the Middletoun Mill was driven at $90°$ to the flow and its position can be seen in the 1877 photograph as already mentioned (page 31).

The lade then ran down through the Middleton Mill though it is unlikely that it drove a wheel here. An outlet at the south-east corner of the mill reconnects the system with the burn.

Though not shown on the drawing, another intake was provided on the east bank of the burn slightly to the south of the outfall from Middleton. This channelled a supply to Paton's Mills which were on the east side of the burn about 70 yards further down.

The whole of this interesting system was maintained by a body composed of the manufacturers representatives and the Town Council (The Damhead Company) and indeed at one time it was the provost of the town who was responsible for climbing up the glen each morning to open the sluice at the dam. It is recorded that after the famous flood of 1877, the cost to the manufacturers of clearing the damhead of debris and effecting repairs was £100[*].

---

[*] Gibson. page 160.

LADE AND WHEEL AT CLOCK MILL

From Bracewell, Harrison & Coton drawing of water power system at Tillicoultry.

Section of drawing dated November 1922 showing property belonging to Robert Archibald & Sons. Map held by Mr Bowie, Chief Engineer, Interbobbin (UK) Ltd., Middleton Mills, Tillicoultry.

Middleton Mills, Tillicoultry.

Existing Mill Buildings

In the course of this study it has been possible, with the cooperation of the mill owners and tenants, to visit all but 2 of the buildings to photograph and make notes on structural detail, constructional techniques and general layout. The interiors of many of the mills evoke a strong 'sense of the past' and indeed to stand in an unrestored attic making notes with the chatter of the looms below almost seems to transport one back to another age - in a few cases even the rumble and vibration of the overhead shafts can still be experienced.

One might well wax eloquent in the description of individual mill buildings, however, the intention here is to provide a factual, unadorned descriptive record of the buildings as they stand at the present day. These individual studies include a summary of the background history where such is available.

MENSTRIE

Background and present use

The only remaining building of what was once a fairly sizeable complex on the west bank of the Menstrie burn is the mill now occupied by the Central Regional Council Water & Drainage Department as a store with offices. Both of the mills which were situated on the east side of the burn - the original mill of the three Archibald brothers and the building known as Forthvale Mill* - are no longer in existence, though the foundations of the latter may still be seen.

The original buildings on the west bank were erected in 1864 by Messers Drummond & Johnston and, following the 'buying out' of Drummond by Johnston after a quarrel some time later, were occupied by the latter until around the end of the century (see page 20). The remaining building with which we are now concerned probably dates from the 1860's though some say that it was built rather later than the other buildings. The position of this building in relation to those which once stood around it is shown on the following page.

Description

The 2-storey building is of rubble construction with a 5-by-14 bay proportion and is located on a north-south axis with the main entrance centrally positioned on the north facade. Being of only 2 storeys and being relatively wide, the double-ridged roof (slated) with a centre valley gutter is particularly appropriate in terms of the overall scale of the building.

The hipped north end conceals the centre valley and supports the clock housing mounted centrally above the main doorway. Two chimneys also protrude at this end though rather out of character and oddly positioned. The chimneys, along with the classical elements on the north facade (doorway and clock housing) are indicative of the later date of this building. Interestingly the clock mechanism has always been maintained and is still in operation providing a reliable timecheck.

The windows are straightforward 12 pane as can be seen in the photograph on page 51 though some have been altered.

---

* See pages 15, 19 & 20.

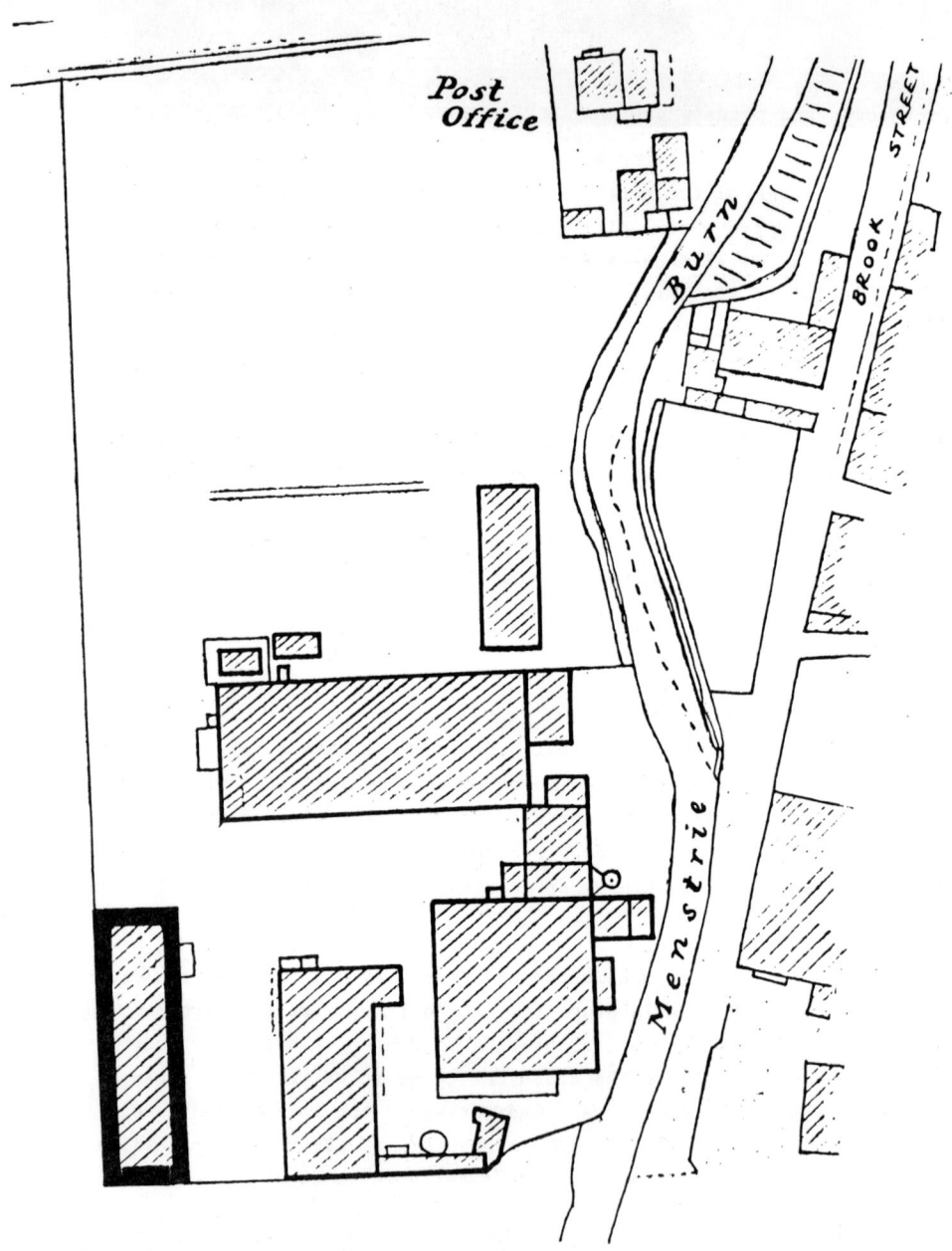

Remaining mill building at Menstrie outlined in black.

Mill at Menstrie viewed from north-east.

North facade of Menstrie Mill.

Clock at Menstrie Mill.

Structure

As with all the mills, the outer walls are of load-bearing masonry construction with double timber cross-beams for the first floor built directly into the stonework. These cross-beams are supported by a single row of centrally positioned 7" diameter cast iron columns at approximately 11'2" centres (bay width). The floor joists are then carried across these main beams; ie. in a north-south direction.

Being of a later date than most of the other mills the construction is rather more interesting than elsewhere in that tension rods are introduced on the underside of the cross-beams. These iron rods run between the twin beams from the column head to 2 brackets bolted to the underside of the beams and then back up to tie in at the outer ends. There are two separate tie rods in the span, one to either side of the central support with the beams cambered over the columns. The two separate tie rods are as one would expect, however, the structural logic for the cambering is not so clear. The system is obviously best illustrated by the photographs (pages 55,56).

The roof structure is supported centrally by a heavy section timber runner supported longitudinally on $5\frac{1}{2}$" diameter cast iron columns carried up through the first floor from the structure below. The roof ties are then supported across from this runner to the wallhead, the valley gutter being formed immediately above the runner.

Present condition

A major structural problem is evident at the south end of the building where substantial brick butts have been erected to retain the gable which threatens to fall outwards (page 57). A considerable degree of movement has already taken place and a further measure taken has been to remove the end section of the main timber runner and replace it with an RSJ tied into the gable.

Timber safe lintels in the upper floor have been removed and replaced by steel angles supporting brick built up to the underside of the timber roof ties.

The regularity of the fenestration on the east facade is broken by the introduction of an external fire escape from the upper level knocked through the fouth bay from the south end, and also by the blocking of

Menstrie Mill - interior.

Column head detail showing iron tie rods.

South end of Menstrie Mill showing substantial brick butts built to resist outward movement.

another window at the lower level to accomodate a flue which runs externally up the face of the building. A doorway has also been formed at the lower level on the east facade.

Internally the front section, which originally housed offices, has been further subdivided by straightforward timber studding running unsympathetically against the columns (page 59).

The problem of deterioration of the main timber runner at roof level (illustrated on page 60) is probably due to inadequate roof drainage. The centre valley is apparently drained only at one point - at the south end of the building. It is therefore likely that the 'run' of this gutter is insufficient. The upper floor remains largely unused except for storage and maintenance is minimal. It is likely that this will lead to further deterioration in the near future.

Timber stud partition/column detail.

Deterioration of main timber runner at roof level.

ALVA

STRUDE MILL

Background and present use

As noted the building now remaining and referred to as the Strude Mill was only one of a large complex in that particular area. The foundations of many of the others may still be seen. Drysdale records that the old mills at Strude were built around 1827 and it is likely that the remaining building dates from that period.

The Strude Mill was occupied by William Archibald and Son up until 1964 when it was closed by them only to be re-opened shortly afterwards under lease to Raymond Hodgson & Co. In 1976 the mill was bought over by Raymond Hodgson & Co. who continue to use the lower floors as a warehouse with offices.

Description

The building is basically a rectangular structure of 6 storeys plus attic with a hipped roof situated in a comanding position over the town of Alva with the Ochil Hills providing an impressive backdrop.

It is interesting to note here the introduction of classical elements into the facade of an industrial building of that period, though with some idiosyncrasy. Four bays in the centre of the building project supporting a pedimented form which in turn supports the bellcote. However, the building is one of 25 regular bays (of approximately 6') hence the 'central' section is offset with 11 bays to the left hand side and 10 bays to the right. The reason for this deviation from symmetry is unclear, particularly since strict symmetry is observed in every other detail, even to the arched openings at either side which are extraneous to the building. While the 4-bay width provides a more suitably proportioned pediment than would, say, a 3-bay width, there seems to be no reason for the imbalance since the whole structure was constructed at the same time. Incidentally, the story that there is a window for each day of the year is not true, even counting the skylights ! *

A clock is set into the pediment as can be seen on page 63.

---

* The Third Statistical Account refers to the east Boll Mill erected in 1847 which had a handloom at each of 365 windows. See page 27.

Strude Mill, Alva from south-east.

Strude Mill, Alva.

Structure

Internally the structure is of pleasing simplicity. Two rows of columns running the full length of the building give a 3-bay width reflected in the windows of the west end. It is interesting that there are no windows in the east gable, perhaps indicating an awareness of daylighting and an understanding of its importance as a design criteria in such an industry. Indeed, being relatively narrow in relation to its length, the building provides, even by todays standards, a highly satisfactory and constant light level throughout.

At ground floor level the columns are in cast iron with independant supporting brackets into which the timber runners sit. These heavy-section timbers run along the length of the building and in turn support the floor joists. From first floor up all columns are 4"x4" timber - probably oak - with chamfered edges, each column being supported directly on top of the runner below.

The roof structure is of 6"x2½" rafters supported at the wallhead and with ties of similar section at approximately mid-height. The inside of the roof is rather unusually lined with a lath and plaster finish.

Present condition

The only external alterations made to the building are the addition of a stair tower appended in an off-centre position to the north facade, the blocking of the three lower windows in the west gable and relatively minor alterations on the south (front) facade at ground level. Unfortunately an inappropriate signboard has been non-symmetrically applied to the building, this being the major visual distraction. Evidence remains of an adjoining building at the west end of the north facade and the regularity at the lower levels is broken here.

The upper floors remain in virtually original condition, a lift shaft being the only addition within the original structure. In the attic storey 2 heavy steel beams have been run between wallheads across the width of the building to support the lift mechanism. On the two lower floors the space has been subdivided but, as in most of these buildings, not in the most sympathetic manner. It is unfortunate that fire and safety regulations preclude the use of the upper floors of this magnificent building. Even as it is an unsightly metal fire stair has been added, extending to the fourth storey, at the north end of the south facade. The building itself is structurally intact and requires rather less in the way of repair than many of the other mills.

Interior of Strude Mill - Original condition.

South facade - Strude Mill.

being a listed building, it is highly unlikely that it will disappear within the near future, but how unfortunate that such interesting and historically intact spaces are so under-utilized. As is so often the case, there is strong conflict here between the requirements of current legislation and the desire to retain the integrity of an historic interior and, as is so often the case again, the space is left un-used accelerating the natural process of deterioration of the fabric.

BRAEHEAD MILL

Background and present use

As discussed in Section 2, it is unlikely that the original Braehead Mill referred to on the 1866 C.S. map is that still in existence. The form of the building itself and the materials used (coursed red sandstone front) would indicate a much later date - a date later than 1886 has already been suggested (Section 2). Apparently the building is now used as a masonic hall, however, all attempts to gain access have proved unsuccessful. As a result, very little information on its background has come to light.

Description

The building (page 68) is of 3 storeys with the main entrances at first floor level and is divided into three 20' bays as can be seen. The slated triple-ridged roof is drained by simple valley gutters.

It might be said that the stairs on the front facade, and particularly the railings, seem somewhat inappropriate to the building as it stands. The shell itself has been much mutilated by the partial or total blocking up of windows with inappropriate materials and the appendage of a single storey brick extension to the rear. The windows which do remain are large 9 pane.

Structure

Inspection was not possible but it is assumed that the structure follows logically the exterior form; ie. column-supported timber beams running the length of the building in line with the valley gutters and in turn supporting the floor joists.

Present condition

From outward appearances the building seems in a reasonable state of repair and is likely to stand for many years, however, it is probably the least interesting of the mill buildings in Alva.

Braehead Mill, Alva.

HANDLOOM WEAVING MILL, BROOK STREET

Background and present use

This small mill (page 70) was built in the early to mid 19th century originally as a handloom weaving mill engaged in the manufacture of shawls. The use of timber posts on the upper floor would suggest the earlier part of the century. It will be remembered that the other mill in Brook Street (now gone) was one of the first in Alva and was also constructed using timber for the uprights. Being for handloom weaving, water power was not a necessity and the building is set at some distance from the burn.

For a number of years now the premises have been occupied and used as a youth club, however, it did remain in use by the textile trade until relatively recently.

Description

The building is constructed of the reddish stone commonly used in the area and is of 2 storeys with a skylit attic (9 pane skylight windows). The 8-bay mill building itself is adjoined by a small 2-storey house, though clearly built at a later date. This is evidenced by the roof detailing and also by the fact that the dividing wall has obviously been an outside gable to the mill at one time.

The internal dimensions of the mill are 48'6" x 30'6" - very small in relation to the mill buildings around, but of course typical for a handloom weaving mill. The half-hipped gable is an interesting feature which is not common in Scotland and which gives the building a squat, dumpy appearance. The form of the windows is also unusual - a 7 pane arrangement as can be seen on pages 70 and 71. This was one of the few buildings for which plans of any description were available though even these were only basic drawings for relatively recent alterations. A reduced copy is reproduced on pages 71 and 72.

Structure

The first floor joists are supported by a central timber beam (8"x6") running north-south which is in turn supported on 3 cast iron columns (not 6 posts as shown on the drawing). On the upper level the main beam is carried on timber posts. The roof is a straightforward timber truss arrangement with the rafters lapped at the ridge - it was not the practice to have a ridge batten at that time.

Handloom weaving mill, Brook Street, Alva.

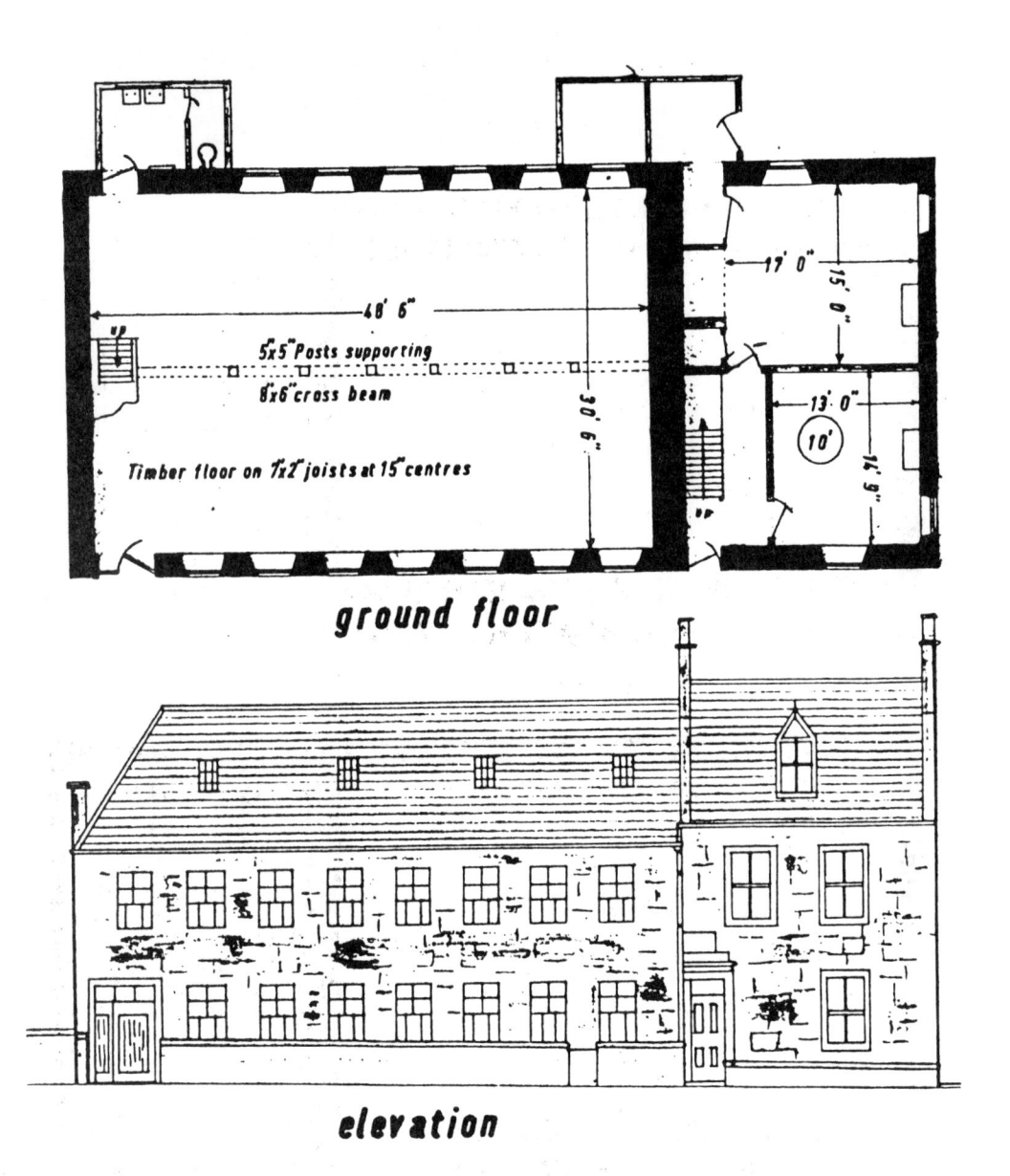

ground floor

48' 6"
5"x5" Posts supporting
8"x6" cross beam
Timber floor on 7"x2" joists at 15" centres
30' 6"
19' 0"
15' 0"
13' 0"
10'
14' 9"

elevation

Handloom weaving Mill - Brook Street.

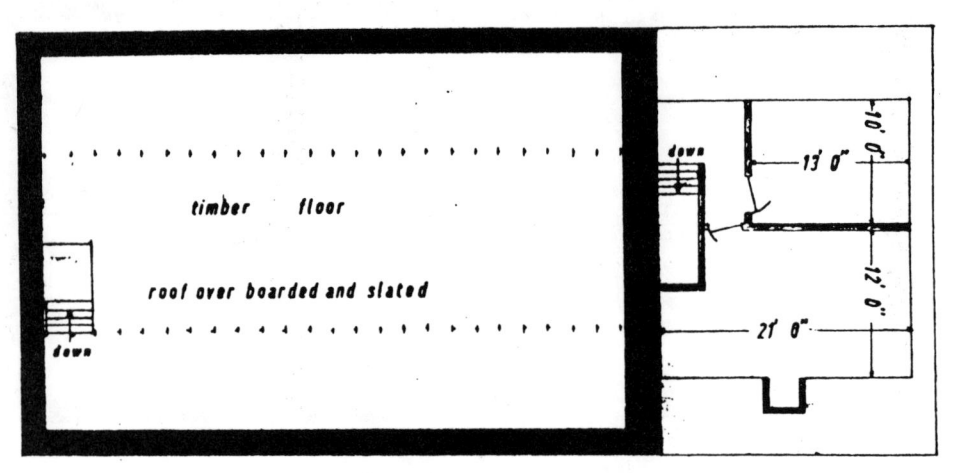

attic

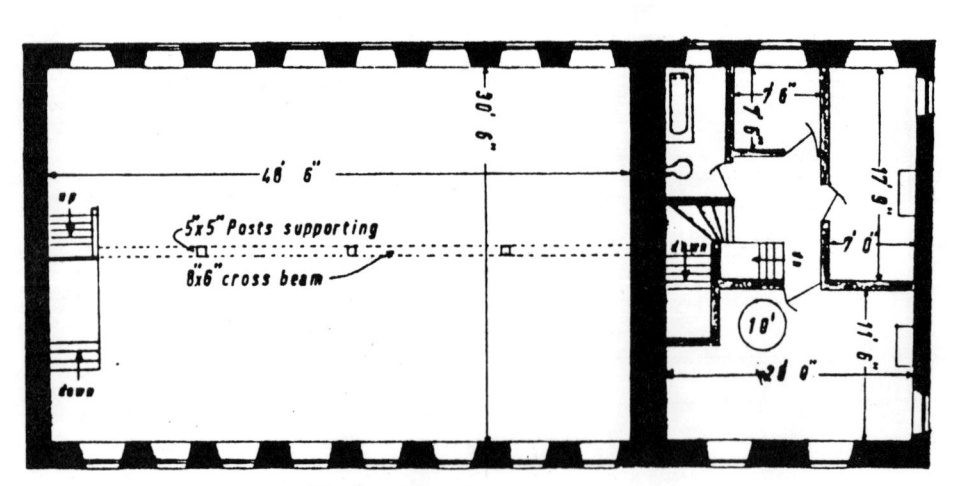

first floor

Handloom weaving Mill - Brook Street.

Present condition

The straightforward rectangular structure of the mill has not suffered any basic alteration, however, various additions over the years have combined to detract from the overall simplicity of its form.

Once again because of fire regulations it has been necessary to knock out both the window on the lower level at the north end of the west facade, and the window at the north end of the east facade at the upper level to provide escape. Both have been executed with little regard to the appearance or materials of the building. Three of the lower windows on the west facade have been blocked in an inappropriate manner, and the addition of toilets on the east facade has necessitated the redundancy of the windows there - some are blocked, others have been opened up and now serve as doorways into the toilet block. The upper windows at this side have now all been built up in brick.

The actual form of the extension itself is completely inappropriate in terms of scale, proportion and materials and further detracts from what would once have been a modest but attractive mill building. Finally, the re-pointing which has been done at some time in the past is most unsightly, being surface-applied without the joints being raked back. This practice, which was widespread at one time, has diminished the visual quality of so much of the stonework around us.

Though not altered to any extent, the general condition of the interior is unfortunate. The youth club members have obviously been allowed a free hand in the 'decoration'. Gaudy colours and weird and wonderful designs are liberally applied throughout. The fabric itself is in need of attention though structurally the building remains sound.

GREENFIELD MILLS

Background and present use

The Greenfield Mill is shown on the 1866 O.S. map (when indeed it did look out to green fields !) and seems to have been of even earlier origin than the mill in Brook Street. The building is located to the north-east of the Brook Street building and nearer the burn. It was at one time water-driven though little other detail now remains with regard to its background.

For some time a blacksmith occupied the premises and it is in this connection that the building is remembered by local people today. It now appears to be a semi-derelict store. The building is illustrated on page 74.

Greenfield Mill from north-east.

Greenfield Mill from south-west.

Description

A simple rectangular 9-bay block of 2 storeys now with a corrugated iron roof covering and in need of much attention. The stonework is random rubble with sections rebuilt and infilled with brick. Windows have been introduced and blocked off at various stages and it is clear from the evidence of upper window openings in the west gable that the building has been reduced in height at some time. The extremely rough nature of the stonework would bear out the suggestion of an early date. The windows which appear most original are 12 pane sash and case at the lower level with 12 pane fixed at the upper level.

Structure

A single row of timber posts supports a main beam running longitudinally, this in turn supporting the floor joists. Unfortunately access to the building was not possible in this case, hence the lack of detailed structural information.

Present condition

A large opening with a steel beam over has been introduced at the east end of the south facade causing the stonework at eaves level to lean dangerously inwards. Indeed the whole building is in extremely poor condition and it seems likely that, should deterioration be allowed to continue, demolition will be required soon from the point of view of safety.

GLENTANA MILLS

Background and present use

The buildings now referred to as the Glentana Mills are located on the north side of the main road at the west end of Alva and are of considerably later date than the mills already dealt with. The CBA record card for the buildings gives a date of 1874, however, it may be that this is based only on a small note on one of the original firm's business cards held in the records of the present occupiers of the building.

Old drawings still exist, these being dated 1887, and have on them the address 83 Bath Stret, Glasgow. The Post Office Glasgow Directory of 1870-71 identifies the occupier of this address as being one Robert Baldie I.A., architect. Whether or not these drawings are for the original building or for additional work carried out with Baldie as the architect is unclear, however, it would seem from the drawings that the former is more likely.

Around 1941-42 the main 3-storey building was destroyed by fire and was then rebuilt as a single storey with flat roof. The original building is shown on the print on page 78 which, though there is a fair degree of artist's licence, generally illustrates the form of the main block. Interestingly the print shows that the old archway through the building had been blocked up though its position is still identifiable.

At some point the original roof with its interesting system of iron ties was replaced with a more conventional double ridged roof with central valley gutter. The drawings done at that time show the original main building to be a 22-bay structure with the arched opening through the 6th and 7th bays from the east end. The upper floor was a semi-attic, the wallhead being at a height of about 3' from the floor. Detailing was as on the powerloom section of the building which still exists and is described below.

Detailed drawings for the Smithy dated 1887 still exist as does the building itself. The boiler house also remains as original, however, the brick chimney was reduced in height when there was a changeover from coal to oil as the fuel. A single-cylinder horizontal steam engine was in operation until a few years ago and remains in position. Interestingly the whole factory was driven (by overhead shafts) and heated by the steam engine with its coal fired boiler for £20 per week in 1961.

The owners until 1961 were Wilson Brothers, known worldwide as high quality weavers for many years. The buildings were at that time known as Dalmore Works. In 1961 the firm of McBean & Bishop took over and are the current occupiers of the building producing scarves, rugs and blankets in mohair, wool and cashmere.

Description

We shall consider only the section which was originally the powerloom shed and which survived the fire of the early 1940's - the other section is relatively uninteresting.

The powerloom shed is the part to the left hand side of the main block on the print on the following page and is also shown in the photograph on page 79. It is a 15-bay single storey building with a semi-basement (used at one time to accomodate the horses) and has a slated, double ridge roof hipped at the west end. The construction is of brick with interesting detailing, particularly at cornice level. The window panels are set back with the windows themselves featured by a light coloured firebrick surround. Those on the gable are arch-headed (page 80).

Old Engraving of Glentana Mills (Dalmore Works).
Artist's impression.

Glentana Mills from south-west.

Glentana Mills from north-west.

Rear of powerloom shed - Glentana Mills.

Detail - Glentana Mills.

There are to the rear of the building single storey sheds of the traditional cast iron column/glazed north light type. These are illustrated on page 84 and can also be seen in the print on page 78.

Structure

The outer walls of the powerloom shed are constructed on a stepped brick foundation reducing from a base of 4' to a width of 23" upon which the 14" solid brick wall is then built. The cellar area has only 5'6" headroom and within this space three rows of brick piers are built. The central row running the length of the building at 12'6" centres support the cast iron columns directly above and are 23" square built on 3'6" square, 18" deep foundations. The two flanking rows of piers support 10" x 5" iron beams which run the length of the building and support the floor at what would presumably be the points of severest loading; ie. where the powerlooms were concentrated below the overhead shafts (the overhead shafts ran down both sides of the building). These secondary piers were $18\frac{1}{2}$" square (p.85).

At roof level the cast iron columns support a 9" x 12" timber beam running lengthwise and in turn this supports continuous 10" x $2\frac{1}{4}$" cross-beams running from wallhead to wallhead. The double roof is then formed of $6\frac{1}{2}$" x $2\frac{1}{2}$" rafters and ties with a 14" deep ridge batten and is glazed between the rafters on the north faces.

This verbal description is better understood if read in conjunction with the photographs of the overall building form and those of detail.

Present condition

The buildings are relatively intact and have not been defaced by the unsightly alterations or additions evident elsewhere. The present use of the premises is likely to ensure that the situation will remain unchanged for some time. The steam engine will be removed soon but fortunately will be returning to Kirkcaldy where it was built to become a museum piece there.

Single storey sheds at north - Glentana Mills.

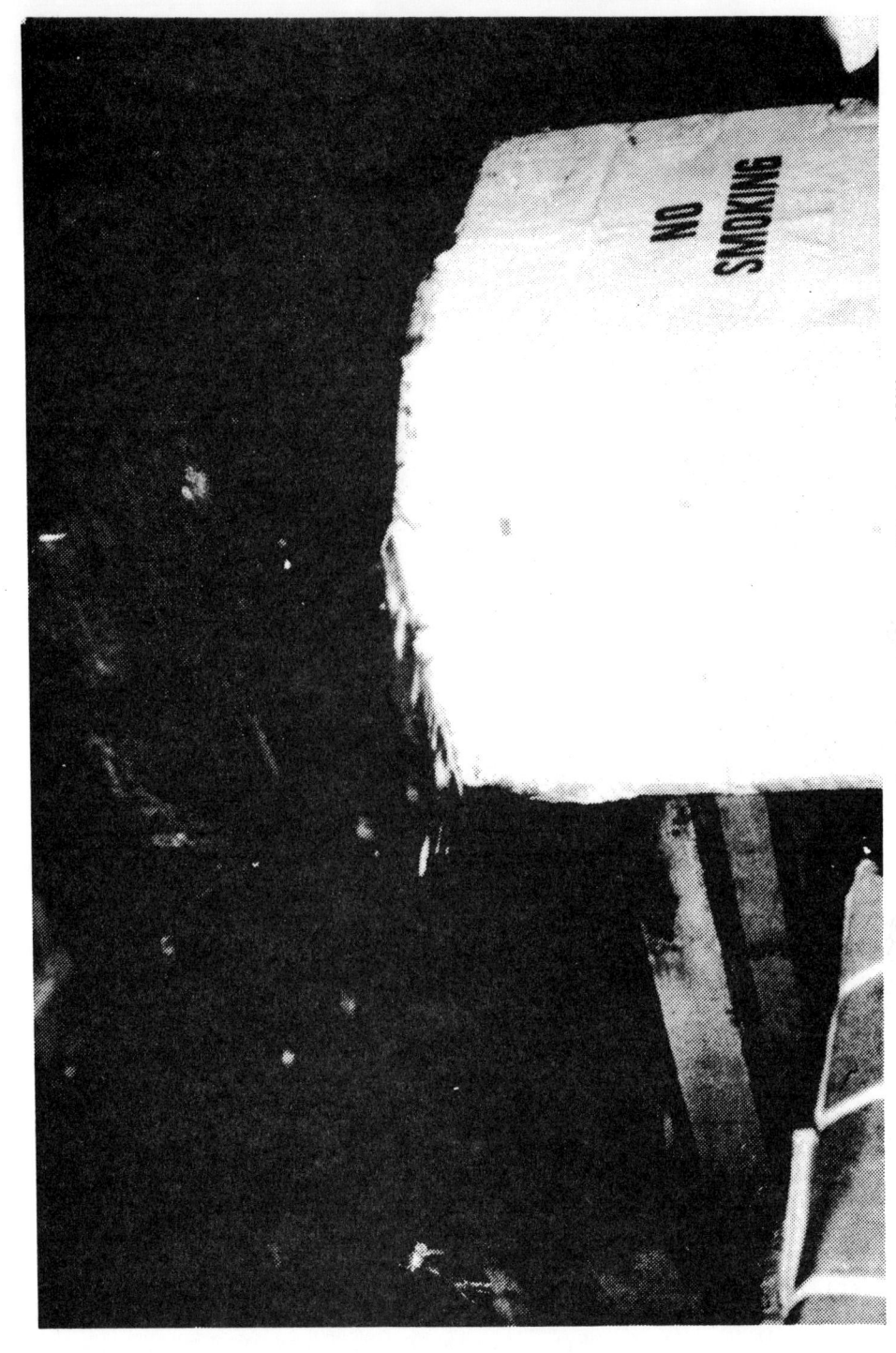

Brick pier supporting iron beam - Glentana Mill.

Interior - Glentana Mills.

Column detail - Glentana Mills.

BURNSIDE MILL

Background and present use

Burnside Mill is situated immediately to the east of the burn on the north side of Henry Street and is opposite what was once Greenfield Mill. Again this building is of a later date, probably towards the end of the 19th century. It was occupied, presumably from its erection, until 1963 by Charles Thomson (Woollens) Ltd., a private company said to have been founded in the 1860's. In 1963 the company went into liquidation. At that time they dealt mainly in scarves, travelling rugs and shawls.

Several months after the closing of the mill it was re-opened to produce shawls and children's wear by 2 young men from Donbros, Alloa and the firm of Kidmars of Glasgow under the name of Charles Thomson (Woollens, 1964) Ltd.* The firm was originally founded in the 19th century on the production of baby shawls. Operations at the mill have continued since 1964 though changes have occurred and the firm is now known as Glen Alva Ltd.

Description

The main building is a 12-bay, 2 storey block with attic and is located on a north-south axis at right angles to Henry Street. It is adjoined to the north by a single storey shed - the loomshop. Another 2 storey block to the east forms an L-shape with the main building. This block is of 7 bays originally with a central doorway to Henry Street and is adjoined at its east gable by a single storey, 5-bay building which now serves as the reception area. All the buildings are of red brick with a buff coloured brick used to highlight detail as at Glentana Mills.

The main block is of 2-bay width with a double ridged roof and the other 2 blocks adjacent to Henry Street simply have the normal pitched timber roof. Of these the 2 storey block roof is hipped at both ends resulting in a rather 'uncomfortable' junction with the main building, the roof being at a lower level. The single storey sheds are of the normal type with roof glazing and have obviously been added to the main building some time after completion - the photograph on page 91 shows windows blocked off in the north gable.

---

* The records of Charles Thomson (Woollens, 1964) Ltd. and of the previous company are available through the National Register of Archives.

Burnside Mill from south-west.

Burnside Mill from south-east.

Burnside Mill from north-west.

Structure

A single row of cast iron columns runs the length of the main block and supports, at the lower level, heavy cross-beams running east-west. On the next level a heavy section timber beam runs on the main axis of the building supporting the joists which run laterally and are built directly into the brickwork. These columns extend through 2 levels only with 6" square timber posts at 12'6" centres (coinciding with the columns) supporting the roof structure.

A 9" x 6" timber runner is carried on the timber posts at a height of 6'7" above the attic floor level. The eaves are 4'3" from floor level (detail at wallhead on page 94) hence the roof sections are asymmetric about the line of the ridge. Rafters and ties are 6" x 2½" at 18" centres. Glazing between the rafters below the ties provides a high level of illumination in this attic space.

On the first floor several tie rods have been added similar to those used elsewhere to take the tension force, however, as can be seen on page 95, these ties do not run the full span of the joists. Indeed it is interesting that the system has been used on a floor joist here - elsewhere it is the main cross-beams which are so strengthened.

The timber safe lintels to the windows are continuous through the brickwork from window to window.

The single storey shed to the north of the main block is a continuation of it and reflects the 2-bay width. 5½" diameter cast iron columns support an iron channel gutter running the length of the building. The brackets at the column heads incorporate adjustable tie rods running across the width of the building as on page 96. Again a high lighting level is achieved by continuous glazing on the outer sides of the roof to the east and west.

Present condition

Over recent years the buildings have been much altered internally this detracting from the simplicity of the structure. As is the case elsewhere, these alterations are none-too-sympathetic though perhaps it might be argued that the building itself is not of the greatest importance with regard to either architectural merit or the growth of the textile trade in the area.

It has been necessary to add a metal fire escape stair from the first floor on the west facade, however, a more unfortunate (and avoidable) change has

Cast iron column and bracket supporting timber beam at first floor level.

Wallhead detail - Burnside Mill.

Tie rod and bracket on floor joist - Burnside Mill.

Column detail - single storey sheds - Burnside Mill.

been the alteration of windows and the addition of a large signboard at the south end of this facade. On Henry Street too doors and windows have been altered which, though attempts have been made to match brickwork, still detracts from the rhythm of the individual blocks.

The structure itself is sound and even at roof level where the construction would appear to make the timbers vulnerable there is little evidence of deterioration.

BURNBRAE WORKS

Background and present use

Burnbrae Works are situated on the south side of Henry Street and slightly to the east of Burnside Works. The original buildings date back to 1867 when the firm of John Gray & Co. Ltd. came into being as handloom weavers. It is assumed that this activity was soon superceded by the introduction of power looms - even 1867 was relatively late for factory-based hand weaving. Later warp knitting became the main activity and though more modern techniques are now used, warp knitting machines are still in the building. At various times throughout their history the original company produced shawls, lacy bed jackets, brushed mohair outerwear and blankets.

John Gray & Co. Ltd. survived to celebrate their centenary, however, the firm is no longer in existence. In 1975 a Mr Thomson from the Burnside Works moved across the road to set up Dolf Textiles, the present occupiers of the building.

It is interesting here to see that the system of overhead shafts is still used to drive much of the machinery, though the shafts are now electrically driven. The buildings which remain are clearly only a fraction of what once existed - the engraving reproduced on the following page gives some indication of the extent of the works.

The manufacturing process now takes place in the lower floor of the original building (the upper floor is disused) and in the single storey sheds to the south. The corner block (to the foreground on page 98) was built in the early part of this century and is occupied by stores and offices, the upper floor again being disused.

Letterhead of John G Gray & Co. Ltd. with early engraving of Burnbrae Works.

Description

The main 2-storey block is situated centrally in relation to the works in a north-south direction fronting onto Henry Street. Another 2-storey block is built to the east and the two are linked by a 2-storey section. This block to the east and the link section were built around the 1920's to match the existing buildings and are of a brick which, from the distance, is similar in appearance to the original (the same as at Burnside). The detailing of the windows in the original block is not reproduced in the later building however.

The buildings to the west of the main block and which also front onto Henry Street are now largely disused, at least by Dolf Textiles. They are 2-storey and again are of the same type of brick as the original. The windows at the lower level on Henry Street have now all been bricked up.

A large 4-bay weaving shed of the typical form is attached to the south gable of the main block and again in this area the overhead driveshaft is still in operation.

The original engine house is now used as a drying room, the engine obviously having been removed. It is interesting to note that the drive from the engine to the main building was a rather complicated set up with a high level shaft running externally between the buildings. Unfortunately a large chimney, which can be seen on page 98, has now been reduced somewhat - its present state can be seen on page 105.

Structure

The 12-bay original block is of straightforward construction with a single row of five 6" diameter cast iron columns supporting cross-beams. The columns are repeated on the first floor and support a timber beam which runs lengthwise and in turn supports heavy timber roof trusses. As elsewhere the width of the building necessitates a double ridged roof with a valley gutter, hipped at both ends.

The section added later to the west is of similar construction, however, in this case the whole of the upper floor is timber lined as can be seen on page 106.

The building immediately to the west of the main block (disused) has an interesting king post roof, however, neglect here has unfortunately led to rapid deterioration.

View along Henry Street - Burnside Mill to left, Burnbrae Works to the right.

Original block - Burnbrae Works.

Interior of Burnbrae Works main block showing overhead shaft.

Interior of single storey sheds - Burnbrae Works.

Engine House, Burnbrae Works showing recess for flywheel on left and bearing for driveshaft on right.

Remains of boilerhouse chimney - Burnbrae Works.

Upper floor of 20th century block Burnbrae Works.

Column head detail - lower floor of original block at Burnbrae Works.

The weaving sheds are constructed of three rows of 6 columns supporting structural iron rainwater channels and glazed timber roofs. The column heads are tied together laterally by adjustable iron rods. As already mentioned the overhead driveshafts are still in operation and are attached, as was normal, to the brackets on the columns and also suspended from the channel section (pages 109,110).

Present condition

The buildings which are still in use are generally sound, including the disused upper floors, however, the buildings at the west are in a poor state of repair with timberwork deteriorating rapidly. The washing and dyeing section, which is still in use for this purpose is also in need of attention. Deterioration here is largely due to the nature of the process, a humid atmosphere being generated.

Little has taken place in the way of external alteration to the buildings themselves, though at one point a large double door has been introduced on one of the smaller buildings.

Internally the inevitable sub-division has taken place however this is confined almost exclusively to the 20th century sections and hence does not intrude into the 1867 building which can still be seen in its original state, even with its overhead shafts.

Driveshaft supported from column brackets in single storey sheds at Burnbrae Works.

Driveshaft supported from channel gutter in single storey sheds at Burnbrae Works.

OCHILVALE MILLS

Background and present use

Ochilvale Mills are on the east side of Alva immediately to the south of the main road through the town. A plan of the works at the present day in reproduced on the following page. The main mill building with which we are concerned is that to the right hand side.

The mill was built in the late 19th century with the red and buff brick common to the other mill buildings of that period, and is similarly detailed. The sheds adjacent are of later date with steel trusses and are not of particular interest to us here.

The mill was owned by the well-known firm of W. Archibald & Son and was closed down by them around 1963-64. In 1964 Raymond Hodgson & Co.Ltd. became interested in the premises and re-opened them around the same time as they re-opened part of the Strude Mill. It may be assumed that, as at Strude, the Ochilvale Mill was not initially bought by them when they began to operate but was leased. The mills are still operated by Raymond Hodgson & Co. Ltd. producing knitwear.

Description

The main block is a 2-storey brick building with a double ridged, slated roof and has appended at either end respectively an engine house and a single storey section which now serves as a mill shop (this is the area indicated as '1' in the plan). This main part is now used basically as a store, manufacturing being concentrated in the single storey sheds.

The building is of considerable length in relation to its width with the regular 6 pane windows providing excellent daylighting standards over the total floor area. The old engine house which drove the overhead shafts running the length of the building is a one-and-a-half storey height space with its own pitched roof and has interesting arch-headed windows and door and circular vent all detailed in brick. A small lean-to shed is in turn appended to the engine house at the south end.

The mill shop has evidently been added to the main structure subsequent on its completion and is again of the same material. The date of 1922 on the steel door between the shop and the main building suggests that the shop may have been added at that time, though an earlier date is more likely. As can be seen from the layout plan it is of irregular shape with a blank brick gable fronting onto the main road.

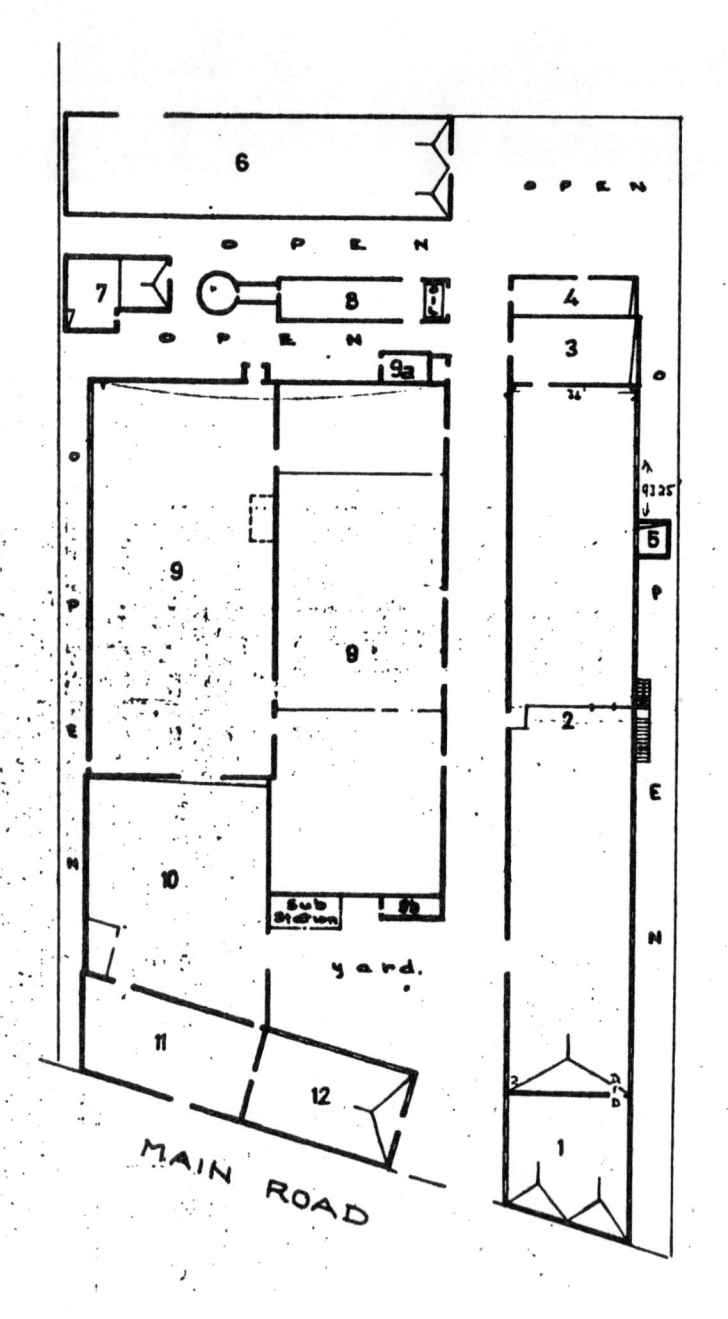

Sketch layout of Ochilvale Mills - main block is to the right. No. 3 denotes the engine house at the south end with the lean-to shed adjacent to it (4).

East facade of Ochilvale Mills

Engine house at south end of Ochilvale Mills

Structure

The external shell is of 14" solid brick with regular fenestration at 6'10" centres. Timber safe lintels bridge the window openings.
A central row of cast iron columns runs the length of the building on the lower floor at 2-bay intervals and these support heavy brackets carrying timber cross-beams which in turn carry the floor joists. A detail of the supporting bracket can be seen on page 116 - the underside of the joists has been sheeted up. The flooring in this case is not as would be expected, but is laid diagonally at 45° to the structure. The ground floor too is in timber and is also laid diagonally, though running in the opposite direction.

In the upper floor the cast iron columns are continued and support a timber runner at roof level. This is jointed over the column heads as required and, as normal, the valley gutter is formed over this beam. The underside of the roof space is completely timber lined (see page 117).

The engine house is of brick with a timber pitched roof hipped at both ends. Two heavy timber beams (approx. 12" x 18") span across the wallheads, presumably to facilitate the lifting of machinery, etc. as well as tying across to the gable of the main block. The inside of the roof is lined as shown on page 118 and is partly glazed.

The mill shop has 2 cast iron columns supporting a timber beam running from the gable end of the main block to the gable of the shop. The roof is lined at ceiling level, however, as can be seen on page 119, the roof ties are exposed. It would seem therefore that the main roof trusses are at approximately 4' centres which clearly indicates further structuring with purlins fixed across the trusses.

Present condition

The north end of the main block has been sub-divided to form offices though the basic structure has not been altered and externally the building remains largely intact. However, small items such as additional doors through existing window openings do intrude slightly into the regularity. Such alterations are more or less inevitable in order to comply with current legislation, but as is often the case, a more sympathetic execution of the work is desirable.

Steam heating pipes are suspended throughout the building however the engine house remains unheated and it is evident that the roof timbers have deteriorated.

Column detail - lower floor, Ochilvale Mills.

Upper floor - Ochilvale Mills.

Engine house roof - Ochilvale Mills.

Mill shop at north end - Ochilvale Mills.

TILLICOULTRY

PATON'S MILL

Background and present use

Coming back to Tillicoultry we return again to the early (and more interesting) days of mill building at the beginning of the 19th century. In 1824 James and David Paton came to Tillicoultry from Alloa to commence business under the name of J. & D. Paton. The firm expanded over the 19th century and by 1882 their works contained 17 sets of carding and spinning machinery and over 250 power and hand looms (Gibson). In 1851 they were awarded the gold medal for their products at the first Great Exhibition in London. In 1859 it was reported in the Stirling Journal and Advertiser that they had "...commenced building a large fine mill, close to their other factory, and also a series of large weaving shops." In the 1860's J & D Paton's mill was said to be the largest in Scotland and was the mainstay of the working population of Tillicoultry.

It is recorded by James Paton himself in reply to the Factory Inquiry Commission (1834) that the original works were erected in 1825 and were powered by water which provided a maximum of 10 horsepower but which dropped as low as 4 horsepower in times of drought. It will be remembered that Paton's was part of the complex water system at Tillicoultry, the inlet for the supply being situated below the outfall from Middleton Mill. Later, as recorded by Nimmo (1880), both steam and water power were used to drive the machinery, water providing approximately 25% of requirements. A newspaper report of 1868 indicates that the steam engine was in operation at that time with a large water wheel for supplementary power.

Paton's were involved in the manufacture of shawls, tartans and tweeds having diversified in the 1850's after a period of recession in the trade. Their products were known worldwide and were worn by royalty on several occasions.

Throughout their history Paton's showed enterprise in experimenting and developing new areas of manufacture and it is suggested by McIntyre that this may well have been the reason for their continued success even through times of depression. In the late 1850's mechanisation was introduced on a large scale. This was immediately after such a period and clearly demonstrates the initiative which they showed repeatedly throughout the century.

The firm still exists as J. & D. Paton & Co.Ltd. and is still managed by
the Paton family, the present Mr Paton (sen.) being a great great grandson
of one of the original founders. Tartans and tweeds are still manufactured
and the firm is now among the oldest in the trade in Scotland. The family
history up to the 1880's is well outlined by Gibson.

The original building having been built in 1825, development subsequently
took place and soon it became the largest complex in Tillicoultry with
facilities for carding, spinning, weaving and bleaching. The siting of
the original mill was on the east bank of the Tillicoultry burn to the
south of the main street, hence at some distance from the others further
up on the west bank of the burn.

The building which now remains is not the original but it is thought to
have been built around 1836. A newspaper report of 6th November, 1868 gives
details of a "Destructive Fire at Messers Paton's Woollen Manufactory".
Apparently the fire originated in the attic floor of what was known as the
Old Mill and which ran in an east-west direction forming the north side
of the large square of buildings lying nearest the village. The fire was
prevented from spreading to the adjacent buildings by the thick gable walls.
As a result several hundred were thrown out of employment.

More recently 2 other large blocks listed as category 'B' in the lists
of historic buildings compiled in 1965 have gone.

These are only a few of the buildings which have disappeared over the years
and those left are the main block of 1836 (also listed category 'B') and
the single storey weaving sheds to the south. The 1836 building is the one
dealt with in detail here.

<u>Description</u>

The building is located on an east-west axis to the east of Lower Mill Street
and is of 3 storeys with a skylit attic. The 34 bay length, a width of
38'6" and 4 levels means that this remaining building is still one of the
largest in the area, Strude Mill being the only one of greater size along
the Hillfoots.

The external walls are of rubble work similar to that elsewhere in the area
though the 6 most easterly bays appear to be of a different stone, more
yellow in colour. The roof is steeply pitched and slated with a regular
series of skylight openings. Rhythm and regularity remains the dominant
effect despite the alterations to fenestration over the years.

Paton's Mill - north facade.

Paton's Mill from south-west.

Paton's Mill - south facade. Note variety of window types.

A central stair on the north side served the building originally and the
general arrangement is best seen at attic level where there are basically
two large areas, one to either side of the stair. It is interesting that
at the entrance to these two rooms at attic level there remain notices with
the following information :

    Room N.º 26   Room N.º 27
    Cubic Space 14,568 ft^3 Cubic Space 19,827 ft^3
    sufficient for 58 persons   sufficient for 79 persons

Not all standards for ventilation and hygiene in buildings are of recent
origin - these notices indicate a standard of 251 ft^3 per person.

Structure

The structure basically consists of the external loadbearing walls and
2 rows of cast iron columns supporting 7" x 5" timber beams which run
lengthwise and support the floor joists. This construction is carried
throughout the building. Timber floors are then laid on the joists and run
along the length of the building. The undersides of the joists have been
sheeted up in most areas. This construction is typical of mill building
in the early 19th century.

The most interesting section of the building is the attic floor. Virtually
no alteration has taken place at this level and while most of the machinery
has unfortunately been removed, one still experiences the atmosphere of a
19th century mill building. The roof is formed from 7" x 3" main rafters
at 23" centres with 6½" x 2½" ties half-lapped to the rafters at a high
level. ¾" sarking is fixed to the rafters with the slates being nailed
directly to it. 9-pane skylights are formed between the rafters at regular
intervals. The ties are supported by timber battens supported on 4" x 4"
chamfered timber posts. These posts rest on timber battens which in turn
rest on the timber floor (pages 127, 128). At certain points the posts are
offset, presumably to provide the extra headroom required for certain types
of machinery.

The old hoist mechanism still remains in position and there are at regular
intervals cast iron grilles in the floor, probably associated with the
heating and ventilating of the attic space. Throughout the working area the
roof is completely lined with pitch pine while in the store area at the west
end the structure remains open.

Present condition

The building remains structurally sound throughout with little evidence of

Column detail - Paton's Mill.

Attic floor - Paton's Mill.

Detail at roof level - Paton's Mill.

Attic floor - Paton's Mill.

deterioration even in the roof structure. The fact that the chimney at the west end is used as a flue to the boilerhouse ensures that the whole gable is heated and this, in addition to the heat rising through the floor grilles already mentioned, may well be the reason for the relatively sound condition of timbers in the attic. This space is now used only for storage and general sorting.

Throughout the remainder of the building numerous alterations have taken place at different times all of which have inevitably meant a loss of the spatial and structural simplicity. It might be said however, that at ground level some interesting spaces have been created by subdivision.

While it has already been said that the rhythm of the fenestration remains the dominant feature of the building, many small unfortunate changes of detail have occurred to detract from what would originally have been a completely uniform facade. Admittedly the window frames would probably have been of a dark colour originally hence detail would not have been prominent, but the fact that the paintwork is now of a light colour highlights the variety of window types, particularly on the south facade (page 124). While the types on the north facade are almost consistent throughout, they are most inappropriate to the building.

Several other small intrusions such as fan outlets, etc. help to break down the unity and probably the worst individual factor is the formation of a large window area on the ground floor at the north side by the insertion of a large lintel.

A cement-rendered, asbestor-roofed lean-to boiler house has been added to the west gable and on this gable several windows have been blocked up.

CLOCK MILL

Background and present use

The mill now known as the Clock Mill was built in 1824 by James and George Walker, the two eldest sons of a Mr Robert Walker who had come to Tillicoultry from Galashiels a few years earlier and who had bought the original Castle Mills in the town (see page 34).

At that time the building was known as J.& G.Walker's Mill for obvious reasons and manufacture was of "...blankets, plaidens and tartan shawls."[*]

---

[*] J.& G.Walker's returns to the Factory Inquiry Commission of 1834.

When water power was introduced it was obviously ideally situated and, as described in Section 3, was incorporated into the water system having a link with another mill immediately to the south-west. It is interesting that the wheel was located, not on the burn side as might be expected, but on the west side. It will be remembered that this facilitated maintenance of the wheel by the closure of a sluice. The power available was about 8 horsepower though not very regular (returns to Factory Inquiry Commission). The water channel and the position of the bucket wheel may still be seen at the Clock Mill and are also illustrated on the drawing on page 46 extracted from the Bracewell, Harrison & Coton drawing of the water power system (see also appendix). A photograph of what remains is reproduced on page 135.

On the death of Messers James and George Walker, the business was carried on for some time by the wife of the latter until her son, Robert Walker, was old enough to manage the mill. This remained the position until at least 1882 when Gibson records that Mr Robert Walker owned this and 2 other mills.

The history of the building in the early part of this century is somewhat vague though it is known that the building did serve as a barracks during World War II. In the late 1940's the mill was secured from the Tillicoultry Quarry Company by Mr Duncan Sinclair who had started work at 14 in Paton's Mill and had also been concerned with Craigfoot Mill. Mr Sinclair involved himself in designing, warp and weft filling, warping, weaving and loom tuning and indeed built his own power loom. He operated initially as a one man business. A newspaper report of 15th April, 1950 states that by that time there were 2 gas-operated looms in the Clock Mill. The business has continued until the present day and is operated by Tom Sinclair, son of the founder. Mohair, travel rugs and scarves are now manufactured at the Clock Mill.

The building is located at the top of Upper Mill Street immediately below the bridge and is listed category 'B' as well as being within a designated Conservation Area.

Description

The structure is a 3-storey and attic rectangular rubble-built building with a simple pitched roof (slated). It is of a 9-by-3 bay proportion and is adjoined at the north gable by a 2-storey house which appears to have been added at a later date though no evidence of when it was added has been uncovered. The house is shown on the 1922 drawing as the ENGINEER'S HOUSE

Clock Mill from north-east.

Clock Mill from Upper Mill Street.

House and Clock Mill from north-west.

Remains of water channel and position of wheel on east facade of Clock Mill.

and at one time was directly connected to the mill by a door from one to the other.

Two features are worthy of special note ; the clock high on the south gable with its ball finial, and the attic dormers on either side of the roof.

The ground floor appears as a semi-basement at the north-west corner due to the slope on which the mill is built and at the north-east corner the floor level is not much above the level of the burn which runs along the east wall.

This east facade, the burn running alongside and the stone-built bridge (also listed) immediately above combine to provide an interesting focus. The building itself is the focal point of the surrounding area terminating as it does the wide sweep of Upper Mill Street (page 133).

The walls are of 2' thick masonry regularly punctuated by windows and, with the 2 rows of columns, might be assumed to give the building internally a 'heavy' appearance. However, the overstructuring in this relatively small building is compensated for by the light quality which, as in most of the mills, is excellent. It is further enhanced by the light-coloured smooth cement render finish to the walls - certainly the most appropriate finish in such a building.

Structure

On the lower floor 2 rows of cast iron columns (at approx. 10'6" centres) with integral brackets support timber beams (approx. 12" x 6") running lengthwise and from these 10" x 2" joists span across at 18" centres from wall to wall. Flooring therefore runs the length of the building. The stair is located in the south-west corner of the building and a hoist shaft runs up through each floor immediately inside the south gable.

The 2 upper floors follow the same pattern though the columns on the second floor are of a different type. Evidence of iron tie rods at each floor level can be seen from outside the building.

The roof is formed with 7" x 2½" rafters at 18" centres without a ridge batten and with 7" x 2½" ties at a height of 7'7" from floor level. The main ties running from wallhead to wallhead and forming the attic floor are 8" deep and floored with ¾" x 6" boarding. 10" broad sarking boards with slates completes the roof. This attic floor is lined internally up to the level of the ties but the ties themselves are left open (page 138). The 2 dormer windows are 12-pane and run from floor level to a height in line with the underside of the ties. They are 59" wide.

Column detail - Clock Mill.

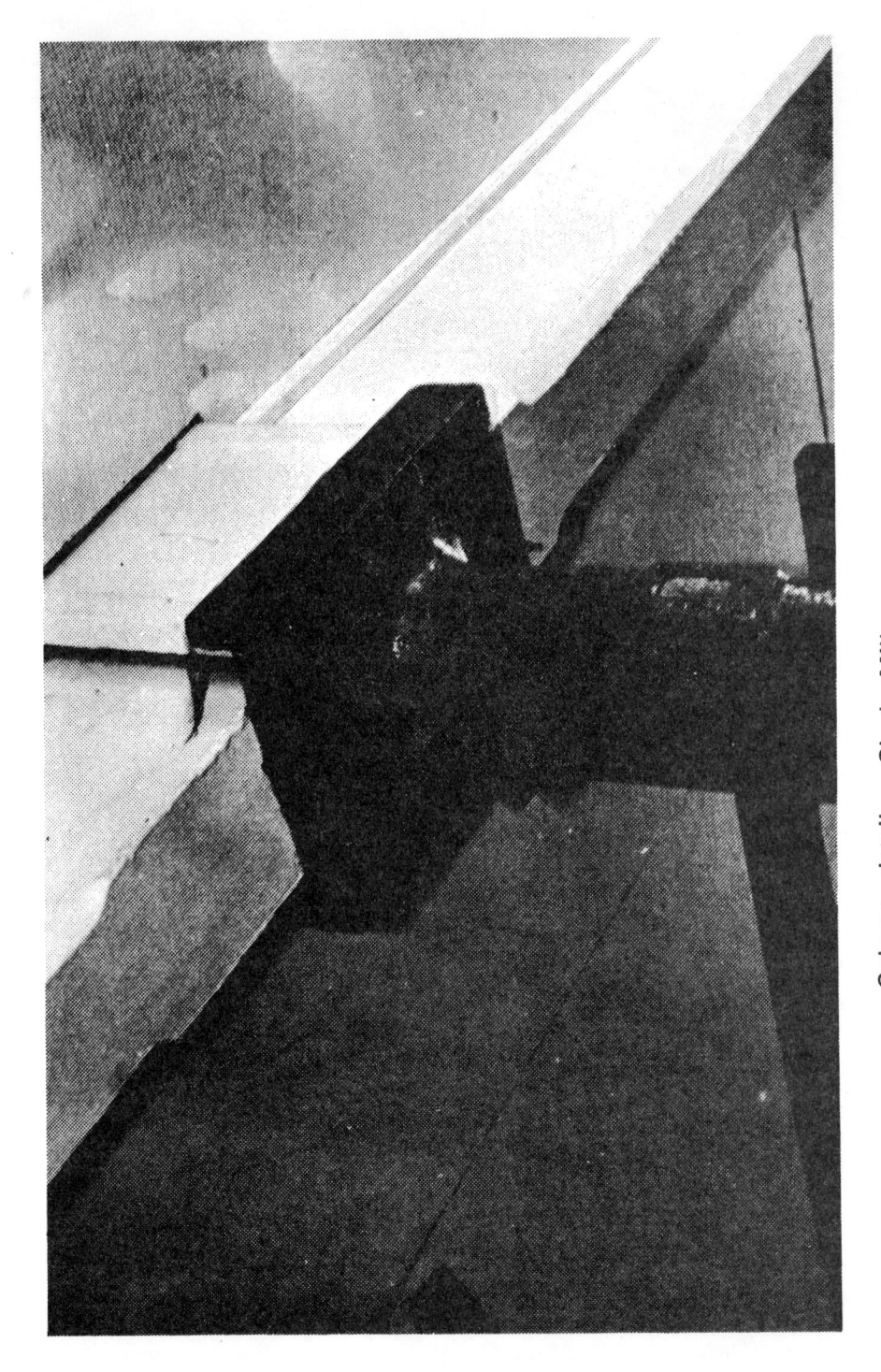

Attic floor - Clock Mill.

Attic dormer - Clock Mill.

A steel structure has been erected within the attic space at the south end over the columns of the floor below to carry the hoist. According to some the attic floor is the haunt of the 'Grey Lady' !!

Present condition

Fire regulations have once again necessitated the addition of various escape doors both on the east and west facades and unfortunately a metal stair has also been introduced at the north-west corner.

The main door on the south gable has at some time been widened with little attention being paid to the appearance - the dressed stone to the left hand side of the doorway has been removed leaving an arrangement which is visually awkward. Interestingly the photograph of the flood of 1877 (page 31) shows a single storey part adjacent to the front of the Clock Mill. This has long since gone and no evidence has come to light as to its origin or purpose.

A small window has also been introduced to the right hand side of the main door and the window further to the right has been partially blocked up. These unfortunate alterations may be seen on page 133.

The house to the north has also been 'defaced' by the appendage of a porch and the addition of a brick chimney alongside the original stonework chimney.

Inside the mill subdivision has taken place, small offices being cornered off with timber stud partitions on the first floor. On the second floor the area has again been similarly subdivided. Only on the lower floor where the heavy machinery is located can one really appreciate the nature of the space within the building as it would have been originally, though even here there have been changes. A small store has been formed in the south-west corner and columns have been removed and re-located. Evidence of the wheel and driveshafts can still be seen at this level.

MIDDLETON MILLS

Background and present use

Middleton Mill was built on the west bank of the burn (the position is shown in the drawing in the appendix) in 1836 by Robert Archibald & Sons who at that time owned the middle-of-the-town mill (Middletoun Mill) and were in need of additional space. As mentioned on page 30, the Archibalds moved over completely to the new mill though still retaining ownership of the old (James Monteath and Alexander Drysdale became tenants).

The mills were subsequently extended by the addition of large powerloom sheds to the south. This extension took place between the survey of 1862 upon which the 1866 O.S. map is based, and 1882 when Gibson was writing. The 1866 map shows only the main mill building and identifies it as a " Spinning and Weaving Mill (Woollen)". As already mentioned it seems unlikely that water power was actually used at Middleton though water was diverted from the burn through the premises for supply.

By the 1880's the mill housed about 100 powerlooms in addition to the many hand looms still being operated at that time. The first self-acting spinning mules in Tillicoultry (referred to on page 11) were housed in Middleton Mills in 1839 having been bought by Robert Archibald & Sons from a Mr Smith of Deanston. The firm produced "...the finest woollen shirtings" in the latter part of the 19th century. The 1922 drawing showing the property belonging to Robert Archibald & Sons indicates that the mills, by now much extended (see 1901 O.S. map on page 26), were still under the same ownership. Shortly after this drawing was prepared the mill was bought over by a Bradford company who operated it for some time then closed it down.

The mill is now occupied by Interbobbin (UK) Ltd. who utilize the space in the single storey sheds but make limited use of the mill buildings themselves.

Description

There are 2 main blocks adjoining each other end to end and lying on an east-west axis. The front block - the one to the east - is narrower and is of 3 storeys with a skylit attic (page 145). There are 2 windows to each floor in the east gable.

The other block is a 4-storey plus attic, 13-bay building, the upper storey being in the roof space with only a small attic formed in the apex

Middleton Mills from north-west.

Middleton Mills from south-west.

Middleton Mills from north-east.

Attic level - front block, Middleton Mills.

Front block - Middleton Mills.

Attic floor - rear block, Middleton Mills.

Single storey sheds - Middleton Mills.

High glazing level in single storey sheds Middleton Mills.

Structure reinforced with steel Middleton Mills.

of the roof. The upper level is lit by continuous glazing between the
rafters as can be seen on page 147. The roof at the west end is hipped
with a single skylight. Other levels have 3 windows in the west gable.
It is interesting that the south wall of this block does not extend to
ground level but is supported on double beams running on 12" diameter
columns. The single storey sheds adjacent extend into the ground floor
area. The walls on both blocks are of the normal rubble construction,
regularly punctuated, and roofs are single ridge timber pitched roofs
finished with slate.

The single storey sheds are generally of the north-light type with cast
iron columns supporting structural cast iron channel gutters. Columns are
braced with adjustable iron tie rods running laterally across the bays.
There are a number of variations in that some of the roofs have been
rebuilt following destruction by fire and others are of a more recent date.
One particularly interesting bay is that shown on page 149 with an unusually
high percentage of glazing. Throughout the single storey sheds evidence
can be seen of the drive shafts once attached to each row of columns.

Structure

The main east block is simply structured with a single row of cast iron
columns extending through 3 levels leaving a clear attic space. The
columns at each level support a main timber beam (see page 146) running
longitudinally which in turn carries the floor joists. The attic space
(page 145) is formed as shown with only a high level tie to the roof
structure. The inside is lined though this has been done at a later date.
The regular skylight openings are formed between the rafters, no trimming
being necessary.

The other building has a double row of 5" diameter columns which support
12" x 6" timber beams again running lengthwise. $7\frac{1}{2}$" x $2\frac{1}{2}$" joists then span
across the building at 18" centres. This construction is continued at the
fourth level though with smaller section timbers. The roof at this level
is timber lined and, as already mentioned, has a continuous series of skylights
on both roof faces (page 147).

Present condition

In the west block the structure has been reinforced in certain areas where
the nature of the material stored has demanded greater load-bearing capacity
(page 150). This work is of relatively recent date. The east block in
particular has been considerably altered at the lower 2 levels to provide
toilet and canteen facilities though the upper levels remain intact and

largely intact. Various window openings have now been blocked up on the
north facade and a fire stair remains at the east end of this facade.
Water penetration is evident at roof level, particularly around the
skylights as may be expected. The upper levels of the west block are in much
the same condition - basically sound but in need of attention to prevent
deterioration - and are also disused except for storage.

The company presently occupying the premises concentrate their activities
in the single storey sheds despite the recurring problems of water penetration
which are almost inevitable with this construction of valley gutter and
large areas of glazing. As already stated, alteration and addition has
taken place throughout the single storey area over many years making it
difficult to identify exactly which parts are original - very little one
would suspect.

DEVONVALE MILLS

Background and present use

The firm of J.& R.Archibald who operated the Craigfoot Mill (page 30)
expanded rapidly in the early 1840's and in 1846 they commenced building
at Devonvale on the north side of the River Devon. This was at some distance
from the mills already clustered around the Tillicoultry burn, however, it
will be remembered that most of the available land in this area suitable
for mill building was now taken up. In any case the presence of a fast-
flowing burn was not critical as it had been in the earlier part of the
century.

The Archibalds operated at both Craigfoot and Devonvale until 1851 when
they transferred completely to Devonvale and proceeded to expand their
premises further. Some of the ancillary buildings are difficult to date,
however it is likely that the main building dates from the late 1860's or
the early 1870's. It does not appear on the 1866 O.S. map (survey 1862)
but is very similar in construction and detail to the Oak Mill erected in 1873.

The change of fashion around the mid-1850's necessitated a change in
manufacture and J. & R.Archibald eventually gave up production of tartans
and concentrated on tweeds. Devonvale Mills ceased the production of
woollen goods in the early part of this century and were occupied as barracks
during the First World War. In 1921 the buildings were taken over from
J. & R.Archibald and re-opened as a paper mill by Messers Samuel Jones and
Company (Devonvale) Ltd. The premises were expanded and continued as paper

mills for many years. More recently the buildings have been occupied by a large furniture warehouse and therefore the public now have access to many parts of the building.

Description

The main building (page 154) is a 16-bay by 3-bay block of 3 storeys with a triple ridged, shallow pitch roof hipped at both ends. The double windows are large with their heights reducing progressively at each level. The proportion of void to solid is indicative of the later date of this building in relation to those already considered in Tillicoultry.

The stone walls are now cement-rendered, however, the stone would originally have been exposed. The sketch reproduced on page 157 is of a poor standard but serves to illustrate the general layout. As can be seen there are a number of buildings adjoining the east gable and running alongside the main block. These are relatively uninteresting, many being structured in steel, and are clearly of a later date.

There was at one time another building which stood independantly in the area which is now used for car parking. It is probable that this was the original mill building which appears on the 1847-48 map.* This building was demolished only a few years ago.

It would appear that the large single storey area to the north of the complex is that which is shown on the 1866 O.S. map. This building still remains and forms another interesting part of the complex. The structure of this area is as described below. Adjacent to the front (west) of this single storey section is a 2-storey pedimented office block facing onto Moss Road.

Structure

The ground on which Devonvale is built, and also the surrounding area, is particularly poor in terms of bearing capacity. Devonvale is reputed to be built on foundations consolidated by the laying of willow faggots at right angles to the run of the walls.

The main building is expressed externally as being divided into 3 bays. This reflects the 2 rows of columns which run throughout the main block and which in turn carry double timber beams running across the building. Those paired cross-beams are set several inches apart and between them run tie rods fixed at the column heads and running over a straining post fixed to

---

* Map of the County of Clackmannan as Politically Extended from Actual Survey during the years 1847-48.

Devonvale Mills main block viewed from south-west.

the underside of the cross-beams. Unfortunately access to the upper floors, and hence the roof space, was not possible.

The single storey area mentioned above consists of 7 bays with cast iron columns supporting roof trusses giving north light. The interesting feature of this structure is the cross-bracing system in timber resulting in what appears to be virtually a space frame in timber.

Present condition

The buildings remain structurally intact and are likely to remain so for many years. Few alterations have been made to the buildings which date back to the time of the woollen mills, however, a metal fire escape stair does intrude on the east gable. What is most unfortunate is the stark appearance given to the building by the application of black and white paint on all external walls and on boundary walls.

The commercial requirement to advertise could also be more sensitively fulfilled - at present 2' high black letters adorn the white boundary wall facing onto Moss Road.

Devonvale Mills main block - interior.

Drawing of layout of Devonvale Mills with main block in foreground and single storey sheds to rear beyond car park.

Single storey sheds at north of Devonvale Mills.

Detail of lateral bracing at Devonvale in single storey sheds.

Roof structure in single storey sheds.

OAK MILL

Background and present condition

Comparatively little information is available on the Oak Mill which is situated on the west bank of the burn well to the south of Paton's mills. This was the last mill built on the burn and clearly the non-availability of land necessitated its erection on a site which at that time would have been well out of the village. Gibson records that it was built in 1873 by a limited liability company and was acquired by one Mr Gill in 1881.

Carding and spinning was carried on at Oak Mill, latterly for Templetons (carpet manufacturers) who eventually took over the building and shut it down. It has been put to many uses since, including barracks during World War II, and is now owned by a local firm, J.Marshall & Sons(Builders)Ltd. Parts of the building are leased by them, the main tenants being a packaging firm who occupy the main block running alongside the burn.

Description

There are basically 2 main blocks with a number of interesting ancillary buildings to the west. The south block on the bank of the burn is a 2-storey rubble-built building of 8 bays length and a 4 bay width reflected at roof level by 4 pitched roof sections running north-south with valley gutters between. On the upper level continuous glazing on all but the 2 outside faces provides a high level of illumination.

The 3-storey north block is of 6 bays length and 3 bays width with a triple-ridged roof running east-west. The windows of this block are double windows similar in detail to those at Devonvale with cast iron support brackets between the windows. Again as at Devonvale the proportion of solid to void is less than in the mills erected in the earlier part of the century. Unfortunately due to the condition of the building access to the upper floors of this block was not possible, however it does appear that at the upper level lighting is supplemented by roof glazing in the normal manner.

Structure

The south block has 3 rows each of 7 columns and these originally supported timber cross-beams running in an east-west direction in cast iron support brackets. The columns immediately above rest on the top face of the bracket and it is likely that the column is simply located on the bracket by a small rounded locating pin. This practice was common in the building of the mills and gives, not a rigid structure, but in effect a pin-jointed frame.

The 5" diameter cast iron columns at the upper level support structural channel gutters which in turn carry the timber roof structure. Tie rods run between the column heads and into the walls at each end (page 168).

The north block is of similar construction to Devonvale with 2 rows of 6" diameter columns supporting paired timber cross-beams with iron tension rods fixed centrally to the underside. The cross-beams are jointed over the support brackets (page 165). The structure on the upper floors and at roof level could not be examined but it is likely to be a logical continuation of the ground floor structure in the normal manner.

Present condition

Unfortunately the south block has suffered from the ravages of various tenants and owners, the most insensitive single act of vandalism being the encasure of all the columns at ground floor level in concrete. The result is a series of 18" square concrete columns, heavy in appearance in relation to the elegance of the cast iron, and from the top of which the original support brackets still protrude. The timber runners have now been replaced with steel beams, no doubt to increase the load-bearing capacity of the floor above (page 161). At the north end a large lift has been inserted and around the building various other appendages have collected over the years, all of which detract from the main block.

The north block is at present empty. A fire in the south-east corner has left much of the timber badly charred. To the west end gable a poorly-designed 2-storey box extension is being added to provide facilities for the local rugby club who have playing fields adjacent. This has resulted in the removal of part of the original gable wall and its replacement in brick (page 164). The effect on the appearance of the building as viewed from the playing fields is most unfortunate (page 163).

Oak Mill - north block from north-west.

Oak Mill - north block - interior.

Detail - north block, Oak Mill.

Detail - north block, Oak Mill.

Detail of concrete column encasure - Oak Mill.

Oak Mill - upper level.

BIBLIOGRAPHY

1. **The Impact of the Rise of Woollen Manufactories on the Town of Tillicoultry in the Period 1800-1861**

    Dissertation (unpublished) by Robert McIntyre BA(Hons). March 1977.

2. **The Industries of Scotland - their rise, progress and present condition**

    David Bremner. (originally published 1869 by Adam & Charles Black)
    Reprinted by David & Charles. 1969.

3. **The Rise and Growth of the Tweed Industry in Scotland**

    Chapter by J.G. Martindale in "The Wool Textile Industry in Great Britain"
    ed. J.G. Jenkins. Routledge & Kegan Paul. London 1972.

4. **Some Eighteenth-Century Developments in the Textile Region of East Central Scotland**

    W.H.K. Turner. article in The Scottish Geographical Magazine
    Vol.69;No.1. April 1963.

5. **The Statistical Account of Scotland 1791-1799 Vol.IX**

    edited by Sir John Sinclair   reissued 1978 by
    E.P. Publishing Limited, Wakefield.

6. **Reminiscences of Dollar, Tillicoultry and other Districts Adjoining the Ochils**

    W. Gibson. Printed by Morrison & Gibb, Edinburgh for private circulation. 1882.

7. **The Devon Valley : Problems of Land Use and Water Supply**

    D. Ronald Macgregor. article in The Scottish Geographical Magazine
    Vol.68; No.1. April 1952.

8. **Imperial Gazetteer of Scotland Vol. 1.**

    Edited by Rev. J.M. Wilson. Published by A. Fullarton & Co.
    Edinburgh. c.1852.

9. **The Tweedmakers - A History of the Scottish Fancy Woollen Industry 1600-1914**

    Clifford Gulvin. David & Charles. Newton Abbot. 1973.

10. The Third Statistical Account of Scotland   Vol.XVIII

   edited by T. Crouther Gordon   Collins,
                                     Glasgow 1966

11. Tillicoultry in Olden Times

   George Watson.   written 1881.   W.M. Bett. Tillicoultry. 1957.

12. Evolution of Pattern Design in Scottish Woollen Textile Industry

   T.A. Stillie.   article in Textile History
                                Vol.1. No.3. December 1970.
                                Published by David & Charles.

13. The Industrial Archaeology of Scotland.   Vol.1.

   John R Hume.   Batsford. London.   1976.

14. Industrial History in Pictures - Scotland

   J. Butt, I.L. Donnachie, J.R. Hume.   David & Charles.   1968.

Primary sources are as referred to in the text and in footnotes

Other references used were as follows :

15. **An Economic History of Scotland in the Eighteenth Century**
    Henry Hamilton. Clarendon Press. Oxford. 1963.

16. **The History of Stirlingshire** (2 vols.)
    William Nimmo. 3rd Edition. Thomas D. Morison. Glasgow. 1880.

17. **Old Clackmannanshire**
    A.I.R. Drummond. R. Cunningham & Sons Ltd. Alva. 1953.

18. **Industrial Archaeology of Scotland**
    John Butt. David & Charles. Newton Abbot. 1967.

19. **Wool Textile Manufacture in Scotland - An Historical Geography**
    W.H.K. Turner. article in The Scottish Geographical Magazine
    Vol.80. No.2. September 1964.

20. **Tillicoultry : A Centenary History**
    E.J. Evans. published by the Burgh of Tillicoultry. 1972.

21. **A Short History of the Scottish Handknitting Wool Industry**
    J.W. Saunders. Alloa. 1943. manuscript held in 'history' file in
    records of Messers. Patons & Baldwins.

                                    Brian A Park
                                    July 1979